Thank you

MW00630350

Tom Laughlin

In praise of *Portrait of a Prairie Woman*

With the perspective of a historian skillfully intertwined with a lifetime of family lore, Tom Laughlin has crafted a fascinating tale of his grandmother Mabel Richmond Green's life as a homesteader in Montana. From a pampered early childhood in Minnesota to the great challenges and learning experiences of life on the Great Plains, Mabel's story, handed down in Laughlin's family through the years, provides personal reflections on our country's growth to the west. This is much more than a family history; it is a rich illustration of the rugged life on the prairie, coupled with treasured relationships that bound the homesteaders together. It is one family's courageous story, but beyond that, it is every family's story of the opening of the western part of the United States. History comes to life through Mabel's experiences expressed so well by Laughlin—a gift to the generations that followed her.

~Anne Gillem, freelance editor and writer; former news editor and reporter, The Associated Press

Portrait of a Prairie Woman

Learning to Love the Land and the People

By Tom Laughlin

Portrait of a Prairie Woman

Manufactured in the United States of America

First printing 2016

ISBN 978-1-939294-43-2

Published by

splatteredinkpress.com

Dedicated to:

The Chinook Coyotes and all their "Pups"

Mabel with her children and grandchildren, circa 1952. Mabel is in back at right center. The author is two years old, far right, on his father's shoulders.

Acknowledgments

Every family has stories passed down from generation to generation and my family has been no different. This book is the result of many stories and many family discussions over the years. Those stories pushed me to research the times and places of my grandparents and great-grandparents. As I did the research I discovered my grandmother's life was special in many ways. But it also was reflective of the hard working, adventuresome spirit of America in the early 1900s. Mabel life summarized the impact of homesteading, World War I, the cultural changes of the Roaring Twenties, and the struggles of the Dust Bowl and Great Depression. Through it all she survived, raised a successful family, and prospered in her life. She was a part of what has made America great.

I could never have written this without the help of my family, especially my mother, Rosemond Green Laughlin Miller. She was one of Mabel's "Chinook Coyotes" and proudly passed along many of the stories. She also had Mary Isabelle Richmond's scrapbook, Mabel's 1914 Diary, and the letters written to Hazel Green. When I started this project she was very excited her mother's life would finally be consolidated in one place. She died in November 2014, at age 93, while I was still doing research, but I know she would be happy I am finished.

Brother Gary and his wife Bonnie read my early drafts and made corrections and suggestions. Gary was the originator of the title *Portrait of a Prairie Woman.*

My cousins, Bob Ayres, John Ayres, and Rick Green, made huge contributions to the book. Bob and John Ayres are Harriet's sons. Harriet, being the oldest, had the best memory of life at the homestead and passed on many stories. Bob and John also have a wealth of knowledge of the central Montana plains. They have made friends with the Baird family, who now own the land, and have hunted on the homestead land for years. They are close friends with the Slonaker decedents and have heard many of the stories passed down from generation to generation.

Rick Green has done extensive research on the genealogy of the Greens and Richmonds and was my main source of detail concerning who belonged to whom in each family. Rick's father, Charlie Green, was always described as the "spitting image" of his father, Harry. If I was trying to imagine how Harry would have reacted to a situation, I drew on my memories of Charlie. Rich also passed on writings and photos of Mabel, Harry and the Green ancestors.

My chapters about Melrose, Minnesota, would not have been possible without the tremendous support and efforts of Roger Paschke and Jeanne Wilber of the Melrose Area Historical Museum. During a visit to Melrose they were outstanding hosts and gave me unlimited access to materials on the Richmond and Conner families in early Melrose. Roger took me to Oak Hill Cemetery where the Richmonds and Conners are buried and also took me to the original farmland where Great-Great-Grandfather Rueben Richmond settled. He pointed out the neighboring land belonging to the Lindberghs, grandfather and father of the famous aviator. Jeanne's contributions were numerous, finding stories in old copies of the *Melrose Beacon* and various pictures and descriptions of turn of the century Melrose. I can't thank them enough.

The Hill County Clerk's Office in Havre, Montana, and the Blaine County Clerk's Office in Chinook were very helpful in tracking down land claims, birth certificates, and other information about Havre, Chinook, and homesteading in Montana. The Chinook Historical Museum also had maps of where homesteads were and who owned what. Finally, Jesse Baird – son of Wes Baird and current owner of the land – was a great host and showed me the spot where Mabel's home was and took me around the area still known as Cherry Ridge.

Jeanette Widen at the Loutit District Library in Grand Haven, MI. was a tremendous help in learning how to use internet resources to find information, in particular Chronaclingamerica.com, which was my main source of old digitalized newspaper articles. She assisted in finding recourses not only about the people in my story, but also about the times and places involved.

My main "cheerleaders" in this effort have been Tom and Anne Gillem, two close friends who are both writers themselves. Any time I got bogged down Tom would tell me to keep going and he read, and approved, my first rough, rough draft. Anne was my chief editor, correcting all my mistakes in grammar and spelling and making sure I had my commas in the right places.

Tricia McDonald of Splattered Ink Press has been supportive and helped me get organized as we approached the task of formatting and printing the final copies.

And finally, I couldn't have done any of this without the support and help of my wife, Jackie. She has heard these stories for almost forty-five years and has read and reread the manuscript numerous times. Words can't express how much I love her.

Table of Contents

Mabel's Story

"Bama," – that was the family nickname for our grandmother – "why did you homestead in Montana? Didn't you have it made in Minnesota? To hear the family stories, you were well educated, had connections, and money. Why move to the Great Plains and start all over again?"

My Grandmother, Mabel Richmond Green Lamb Holmes (she was married three times and outlived all her husbands) was eighty-eight and living in a nursing home in Spring Arbor, Michigan. All the grandchildren had grown up with stories of Bama homesteading, living on the prairie, and giving birth to her children in the isolation of north-central Montana. We had all heard of raising five children on her own after Grandpa Green died, and we all knew how successful the family had been. I wanted to know the whole story, so I asked her to tell me one more time.

"Oh – Those were the happiest days of my life," she said with a distant look in her eye. "I had come from a good background, but those years in Montana shaped my life and made me who I am. It was where I met the love of my life and started my family. And it was a beautiful spot. In my memory I see vast fields of waving grass and grain, the prairies stretching for endless miles to the Little Rockies or four other ranges that formed my horizon, the royal purple mantle of acres of blossoming alfalfa or dazzling blue of flax."

"Sounds beautiful," I said. "But it must have been tough. You were miles away from town and civilization. Didn't you miss that?"

She nodded. "Oh yes, there were hard times. Watching the terrifying glitter of an approaching cloud of grasshoppers on its way to destroy every green blade of grass or grain; closing up our houses against a storm; groping our way through blinding blizzards by following a rope from house to barn; fighting floods and prairie fires and enduring the agony of waiting for a doctor. To balance these are the happy memories of loyal friendships, shared joys, and blessed companionships. Every neighbor, even many miles away, was a friend and all shared happiness and troubles. I would gladly welcome them all again."

She looked up at me with a smile. "You want to hear it all? It's a long story."

I smiled back. "Yes, Bama. I'm not going anywhere. Tell me the whole story."

"Okay. Take good notes."

I did. This is her story.

The Havre Land Office: 1913

My story begins on March 10, 1913, in Havre, Montana, at one of the most significant moments of my life.

In the early morning light, Mother and I walked toward the Havre Land Office and saw a long line of men snaking outside the office. My father had been out of town on a business trip and had sent word for us to meet him there. We were astonished to see eager land seekers in a line over half a block long.

"Papa, where are you? E. C. Richmond? Are you here?" I called over and over as we went down the line.

"Mother, are you sure Papa is here? It's only Monday, and we can't file until Wednesday. Maybe he didn't know there would be this many people in line. Maybe he's not here. Then what will we do? Look – the line is already halfway around the block!"

"He ain't here little lady!" yelled a man at the back of the line.

"He missed the train, girl," yelled another.

"I think he overslept."

Mother wore a neat black skirt that stopped at the top of her heeled boots, but dust still billowed up behind her. She wore a starched cotton blouse with a high lace collar and a black shawl to protect her from the morning chill. Her curly brown hair was done up in a bun and tucked neatly under her small winter hat. Her dress and her perfect posture made her stand out against the rough and dirty clothes of the men in line. In spite of her small delicate features and proper ways, she was tough and confident. I, on the other hand, was dressed casually, in a brown, ankle-length dress with buttons running up to the collar. My boots were laced high about my ankles and I wore a wool overcoat since it was still winter on the Plains.

Mother gave me a stern look. "Ignore these fools, Mabel. If your father said he would be here, then he will be here. I've learned to never doubt him. Just keep looking."

We entered the Land Office and still didn't see Father. We nervously followed the line up the stairs and down the long corridor to the office. There, sitting patiently by the door, was my father. "Here I am, Mabel," he laughed.

"Papa! You're at the front of the line! How did you get here ahead of everyone else?"

"I'll explain later. Right now just sit here and keep quiet."

I did as my father ordered and took a place next to him. As I did, I looked back and surveyed the faces of grown men grumbling and glaring at me with jealous eyes.

In two days a new section of prime prairie land in north-central Montana would be opened for homesteading under the Enlarged Homestead Act of 1909. If a person was over twenty-one and a citizen of the United States, they could claim up to 320 acres of land and, after three years of residence, file for the deed to the land. My family wanted to get in on the opportunity, and somehow my father had managed to get the first spot at the Havre Land Office. When it opened

Wednesday morning, I would file a claim for my new home and get a piece of rich, High Plains' soil.

It was Monday, so I had two days of waiting. It gave me time to think back to how I got to this point in my life.

E.C. Richmond

My earliest memories are of growing up in Melrose, Minnesota, and my parents. Most of all, I remember my father, Edmond C. Richmond, better known as E. C. He was an imposing man. Almost six feet tall, with strong arms and a barrel chest, he could look down on most people. His most imposing trait though was his ever present confidence and domineering personality. He was direct, blunt, and never afraid to express his opinion. He loved to talk and tell stories, and most of my early years are remembered in the stories he told me.

His early life was shaped by his father, Reuben Richmond, constantly moving to find a new and better place to live. Edmond was born in Indiana in 1852, and by the time he was four years old, the family had moved west to Minnesota. Grandfather Reuben was an early pioneer in the land west of the Mississippi River, helping to found the village of Richmond two years before Minnesota became a state in 1858. They settled on a farm a few miles from the small fort built for protection from Indian attacks. The need for the fort became apparent in 1862 when the Dakota Indian War erupted in Minnesota.

The Dakota people of southern Minnesota went on the warpath when the government tried to force them because onto reservations. The Civil War was being fought and the soldiers were away, so the Indians took advantage of the shortage of manpower. The raids and fighting spread north quickly and everyone was warned to take shelter. While Grandmother Richmond and Edmond's sister, Harriet, went to the safety of Fort Richmond, Grandfather Reuben and Edmond stayed back to pack the important belongings on the wagon.

My father would then make a dramatic pause as he told the story. "You know, I was only ten," he would say. "We loaded the wagon but it was late, so Grandfather Reuben decided we would spend the night in the cabin. In the pitch dark of night nothing felt right. It was unusually quiet and calm. We knew the natives were near. We had seen feathers and heads on the far side of the fields. I was terrified, sobbed for my mother, and could not sleep, so my father decided to start out early. About five in the morning we hitched the horses and headed out. Our cabin was in a low valley and the road climbed a long steady hill. Upon reaching the top of the hill we paused and looked back at our cabin. To our shock it was in flames. The Indians had not waited for dawn to attack and quickly burned us out. When we arrived at the fort, I realized how close we had come to being killed. I will never forget it. I shudder at the memory, even today."

The Indians were finally defeated and forced to move west so Grandfather Richmond decided to move once again. He lived near the rapids of the Sauk River, near the present city of Sauk Centre, Minnesota. Then, in 1868 he moved down river a few miles to the new village of Melrose. Their land was west of the village along the Sauk River. Their neighbors were a family named Lindbergh, who had moved to the area a few years earlier. Father became friends with the Lindbergh's son Charles, who would go on to be a political leader in the state of Minnesota. His son, Charles Jr., was the famous aviator who flew to Paris in 1927.

As a teenager, Edmond worked for the Great Northern Railroad keeping track of the horse teams as the railroad worked its way through western Minnesota. He watched the rail workers, in particular, the carpenters and craftsmen responsible for building support buildings. He would help, whenever possible, in order to learn their trade. By the time he was eighteen he was skilled enough to start doing carpentry on his own. Within a few years he started "E. C. Richmond – Contractor" and had a reputation as a skilled builder in the town of Melrose and Sterns County. By his middle twenties, he had his own planing and sash mill to prepare lumber. He built schools, commercial shops, bridges, and private homes in Melrose, Sauk Centre, Fergus Falls, Meiers Grove, Long Prairie, and many other locations throughout Sterns County, Minnesota. By 1896 his skills had earned him the contract to build The Hotel Melrose at a time when the Great Northern Railroad was bringing more people into the city. It was the largest building in town for many years.

"E. C. Richmond – Contractor" became one of the most successful builders in central Minnesota. Father gained a reputation as a hard businessman and a tough competitor in bidding jobs. But he also was known as a businessman who produced a fine finished product. The *Melrose Beacon* said, "His contracts are always filled to the letter, and his work accepted without question." The Sauk Centre paper said, "Ed is a good workman and is successful in getting a large propor-tion of the building in town." And after completing a new school in the village of Avon, the Trustees desired "to make public acknowledgment of the faithful manner in which he performed his contract."

Father was very active in community organizations. He was a member of the Melrose Masonic Lodge and was elected Grand Master of the Lodge. He represented both the Masons and the city of Melrose at statewide conventions at the state capital of St. Paul. He was also a leader of the local Elks Lodge. As his business and reputation grew, he became more involved with civic government, often serving on political committees.

Father often touted the business advantages of living in Melrose. He would tell everyone, "We need to keep growing and progressing. We must take advantage of our position on the rail line. The Great Northern Railroad gives us high quality transportation to get our goods to market in St. Paul, Duluth, or even as far as Chicago. We need to use it to our advantage."

He often promoted a new school for Melrose. "We need a new public school with all the modern facilities. I have built schools in surrounding communities – Cold Springs, Lake George and Long Prairie to name a few – and I've seen the impact on those places. We need a new school here in Melrose to keep up with our neighboring communities."

He felt strong enough about the direction the city was going by 1896 to run for president of the city council of Melrose. He won the election 194 votes to 132 and was president of the council for the next two years.

Father loved excitement, crowds, and action. He never passed up a challenge and bragged about his successes. He could be loud, rude, and boisterous, but he could also be kindhearted and giving, especially to his family and close friends.

For all his success as a builder, he was not a great businessman. He loved a challenge and was willing to take a risk if he thought it would lead to more recognition and success. He was not afraid to gamble or speculate on a project based only on his instincts. He had some profitable investments, but also some costly failures, which is why my mother was so important to him. She stabilized him and was his anchor.

My mother, Mary Isabell Conner Richmond – known to most as Belle – kept Father grounded. She was his chief supporter and business partner. Her family – the Conners – had come to Melrose even earlier than the Richmonds and, according to family lore, had a lineage that included Ethan Allen of Revolutionary War fame. My parents met in school and were married in 1874, when he was twenty-two and she was seventeen. It was a very good marriage.

Mother was a handsome woman of average height with beautiful brown hair and piercing, deep-set brown eyes. She was intelligent, loving, and well educated. She was the only person who could stand up to Father and control his energy. She had an excellent business sense and was a key to the successes of "E. C. Richmond – Contractor". She kept the books and watched the finances, keeping Father from speculating too much or too fast.

Mother loved the theater, played piano, and had an exceptional voice. She was a regular actress in the community plays and sang in the church choir. She frequently was asked to play or sing at weddings and other events. Mother would organize dinners and other social events for friends and the entire community. She was very active in the Episcopal Church, where she was president of the ladies' guild. She was an officer of the Lady Maccabees, a benefit society that provided life insurance for widows and single women. Mother also organized masquerade balls, excursions to Duluth and St. Paul, and hosted New Year's parties for the community. The *Melrose Beacon* frequently mentioned her activities and travels in the society section.

My mother was polite with impeccable manners, however, she could be steely tough and loved the outdoors. One

My Mother

Mary Isabel Richmond

time she spent two summers living in a primitive cabin near an Indian reservation on Leech Lake to hold down a land claim Father made. She became friends with the natives, learned their language, and even traveled the lakes in a birch bark canoe.

My parents wanted children, but Mother had a hard time getting pregnant. Finally, after ten years of marriage, Mother gave birth to a lovely little girl in 1884. They named her Harriet – Hattie – in honor of Father's sister. They treasured the little lady, but she was never very healthy and despite their best efforts, little Hattie died in January 1889. The doctor said it was the croup, whatever that is. She was only four years old. The *Melrose Beacon* gave a brief death notice and stated "The bereaved parents have the heartfelt sympathy of this whole community." Her death devastated my parents. Belle was thirty-one. They didn't think they would ever have another child.

However, by the grace of God, Mother became pregnant again and I was born April 7, 1890. I was baptized four months later – August 17, 1890 – at the Trinity Episcopalian Church in Melrose. E. C. and Belle had been devastated by the death of my sister Hattie, so my health was closely monitored during my childhood. Many family friends told me Mother would do anything to keep me from getting even a simple cold. As their only child – at a time when most families had many children – I received their absolute attention and thrived on it. Mother taught me all the finer aspects of being a lady. I must admit, I was spoiled. My parents bought me fancy clothes and took me to all the best places. As a result, I was expected to be a lady and be comfortable in public. From the moment I could walk and talk, I was taught to be polite, respect my elders, use proper grammar, and dress correctly to fit the occasion.

It was a lively, exciting time and place to grow up and my parents were in the center of it all.

Melrose: 1890-1906

Melrose was a thriving city in the 1890s. It was first settled in the late 1850s, growing up around Edwin and William Clark's Grist Mill at the dam on the Sauk River, but when the railroad came to town in the 1870s it grew rapidly and became one of the key cities in Sterns County. It was in a lovely valley of the Sauk River, half way between St. Cloud and Sauk Centre, and surrounded by fertile farmlands, refreshing lakes, and thick hardwood forests. The forests provided a steady source of lumber for Papa's planing mill.

Each season had a special beauty and character. Spring was filled with refreshing rains, delicate blossoms in the apple orchards, and fragrant wildflowers in the fields. The warm summer days were perfect for picnics by the Sauk River, boating on the lake, and walks in the parks. The long days also made summer the best time to travel and visit relatives and friends. Autumn harvests brought their own unique sights and smells, as the fields and meadows gave up abundant harvests of hay and wheat. Winters were cold and crisp and the perfect time to enjoy the theater and plays in town.

By the turn of the century, Melrose was an exciting, growing, community. It had a population of almost eighteen hundred and all the modern amenities. Electricity arrived in the 1880s and the first telephone lines were put in shortly after I was born. My father, who always wanted to be first and have new technology, had one of the first telephones in town. We were "Number 6", although all you really had to do was tell the operator you wanted to speak to E. C. Richmond and she would connect you.

Melrose had a large rail yard, a roundhouse, and was regional headquarters for the westward expanding Great Northern Railroad. The railroad was a sign of strength and prosperity. It brought new products, shipped out commerce, and brought news from the rest of the country. The railroad was the largest employer in Sterns County. Daily activities were scheduled around the railroad timetable. Every business, no matter how small or seemingly insignificant, was affected by the railroad. A profit was made or lost if your product got on the train on time. Although dirty, smoky, and noisy, the trains had a majestic power and beauty about them that permeated the entire community.

Main Street was a wide, straight, thoroughfare running east and west and lined with a wide assortment of stores where Mother and I would shop. There was Lambert Merchandise, Rehkamp and Stundebeck Merchandise, and of course Mr. Borgerding's large store for shopping and dreaming of fancy clothing. If they didn't have what you wanted they would order it from Minneapolis or St. Paul and have it within a week. There were grocery stores and Mr. Ahearn's jewelry store. He sold and repaired watches, and also sold bicycles. Melrose boasted of Mr. Hoeschem's flour mill, three banks, a creamery, a newspaper, Mr. Helsmer's drug store, and an opera house, which I loved.

It had the typical contrast of spiritual and sinful. There were five churches: St. Patrick's for the Irish Catholics, another small Catholic church, St. Boniface, for the Germans, then churches for the Lutherans, the Methodists, and Trinity Episcopalian, where my parents attended. And, of course, it had upwards to fifteen saloons, four focused on Irish traditions and two beer gardens for the Germans, where the German language newspaper and a healthy conversation in German could always be found. The city also four hotels, but the largest was The Hotel Melrose, Father's proud accomplishment. It had forty-five rooms and was considered one of the finest establishments in northwestern Minnesota. Father and Mother were active in many civic organizations like the Masons, Elks, and Knights of Columbus. The railroad connected us to the state capital in St. Paul, the mills in Minneapolis, the shipyards in Duluth, and the stockyards in Chicago. It was a prosperous, comfortable town in which to grow up.

My early years in Melrose were marked by education, luxury, and learning how to properly conduct myself. Mother was a strong proponent of learning at every level. She would teach me herself when school was not in session. She was a stern, but fair, teacher. She did not believe a young lady's education should be any different than a young man's. Therefore, I learned to read and write long before I entered the public schools, and I was expected to excel in all my classes. I was reading the classics by the time I was ten, and Mother drilled me on mathematics every night.

However, my favorite time was when Mother gave me music lessons. I grew up in a household filled with theater and music. Shakespeare, Beethoven, and Bach were constant companions. Mother and I practiced piano and voice every day. She was patient, but disciplined, in her lessons. She did not allow me to play another piece of music until I mastered

13

her assigned piece. I was singing in church by the time I was five or six, and had roles in community theater before I was eight. At age twelve I won an award dressed as Little Lord Fauntleroy at the Masonic Temple Masquerade Ball. I loved the velvet jacket and knee pants, but the best part of the costume was the fancy blouse and large lace collar.

Father did his part to spoil me, always returning from business trips with gifts and showing me, with pride, his numerous construction projects in the county. He bought me a bicycle when I was eight years old and taught me to ride so I could show it off in town. He decorated it with small ringlets of wood shavings for a Fourth of July parade and I won the prize for the best decorated bicycle.

Father could be stern and serious, but also childish and mischievous. He loved playing games and enjoyed being around children. Each winter he would make toboggans in his shop, then take them to the local sledding hill and give them away to appreciative children. But first he would have to jump on the toboggan himself and fly down the hill, "just to test it," he would say with a laugh. He loved to ride around the streets of Melrose on his bicycle, weaving back and forth in the streets without a care in the world.

When I was old enough, my parents included me in many of their social events. I regularly attended the dances and masquerade balls at the Masons, the Episcopal Church, and the Lady Maccabees. I even won a competition for best masquerade at the New Year's Ball when I was thirteen. Oh, it was such fun.

Looking back, I realize how lucky I was. My father was very successful, and we never wanted for money. Our house was in the best section of Melrose. It was not the largest in town, but was very comfortable with electricity and running water. Mother and I dressed in the latest fashion. I loved dressing up in silk and lace, wearing white gloves and jewelry. My hair was always done perfectly. Mother made sure I looked and acted like a lady at home and in public. I loved it.

Father was frequently away from home. If he wasn't building or inspecting a project, he was hunting or fishing. He was an avid outdoorsman. An excellent shot, he taught me to shoot at a young age. Papa was very successful in shooting competitions and was the champion shot of Sterns County. He loved to take me along, always telling me I was his good luck charm.

"Mabel," he would say, "I always win when you are at my side." Once, when I was about twelve, I was unable to attend the Sterns County Glass Ball shooting championship. Father came home in the evening totally frustrated. "I only hit twelve balls out of thirteen possible in the championship round. I almost lost to Harry Kalkman, Jr., but he missed the last shot. So we tied and the shoot-off is tomorrow. Mabel, you must be there to bring me luck."

The next day was cloudy with a light drizzle of rain when we showed up at the shooting range. There was a larger than normal crowd since Mr. Kalkman had been talking about how he was going to beat E. C. Richmond at shooting. No one had come close to Father in the last three years, and Mr. Kalkman thought he would be the one to do it. He was bragging throughout town of how they had tied and how he was going to become the champion. Father listened to the chatter and did not say a thing, but I saw his face take on a steely look. I knew it was one of deep concentration and desire to win.

The competition was simple. The officials threw up glass balls, one at a time. Each contestant had two sets of twenty-five shots, and the best score out of fifty was the winner. Father shot first. The drizzle and cold seemed to bother his shot more than normal and he only hit twenty in the first round. Mr. Kalkman responded in his first round with a score of twenty-one. You should have heard his hooting and hollering. "I'm going to beat the great E. C. Richmond. I will be champion!"

Mr. Kalkman shot first in the second round and hit nineteen balls. Although not as good as his first round, he still crowed about what a great shot he was and how the trophy was his.

Father came over to me and whispered, "I've got him. He will not beat me. Give me a kiss for luck." I kissed him and he went to the shooting line. Even in the cool evening air with the drizzle continuing to come down, he promptly hit twenty-two balls, to win the championship with forty-two successful hits.

Due to Father's frequent absences, I became Mother's companion and confidante at a very young age. Mother doted on me excessively – I'm sure the loss of Hattie had a lot to do with her constant need to have me close. We went everywhere together. We shopped together, went to plays and opera together, and traveled together. Consequently, I did not have many playmates my own age. I had friends and acquaintances, but no one as close as my mother.

Mother was artistic and taught me appreciation for the simple things. If we were taking the train to my aunt's in Fergus Falls, she would say, "Today let us notice people's eyes, ears, or noses." Or if we had a longer trip to St. Paul she might say, "Let's see who can see the prettiest or oddest person." If we were riding through the woods in our buggy behind our buckskin horse, Sam, she would tell me to "look for the straightest or tallest or most crooked trees, the different birds or flowers." She taught me to observe, compare, and most of all, appreciate life.

She wanted me to experience nature and community as much as possible. When Mother had to go to St. Paul for an Eastern Star convention, I went with her. We traveled to Duluth, Milwaukee, and Chicago to visit museums, shop, and listen to opera. We always rode the train in first class to visit relatives in Green Bay, Fergus Falls, Leech Lake, and even as far as Indiana. She was comfortable in both big cities and the wilderness. She loved to walk in the woods, go on picnics, and canoe the rivers and lakes of northern Minnesota. Mother always made sure to include an educational element wherever we went. By the time I was sixteen, I had experienced most of the major sights of Minnesota and western Wisconsin. Through all of this she kept her patience and continually showed me love and understanding. She became my best friend.

Mother was very proud of her background, her community, and her family. It was undignified to brag about family in public, but she quietly and meticulously kept a scrapbook of events in the lives of the Conners and the Richmonds. For years she recorded every birth and death in the family, from my sister Hattie's birth and sad passing, my uncle Reuben's sudden death from a heart attack, the wedding of her sister, and the death of Grandmother Conner. She pasted newspaper articles about social events our family participated in – masquerade balls, church socials, Masonic dances – and Father's construction projects. And she kept writings and poems she found motivating and inspirational. This scrapbook became her record of our family's accomplishments.

She was forced to slow down her active social life in 1895 when she was taken ill with rheumatic fever. We were all concerned for her health since the dreadful disease was known to affect the heart. After several weeks under the skillful care of Dr. Campbell she recovered and seemed to be fine. However, she frequently became fatigued and short of breath after only moderate activity. She refused to let it influence her civic activities though and continued to volunteer for many events in town.

Father's increased business and reputation for quality construction marked a significant change in his life. First of all, the leadership of the Great Northern Railroad noticed his work. During the 1880s the Great Northern had expanded into Montana and finally completed the route to Seattle in 1893. It needed new rail stations and equipment buildings and Father became one of many local contractors to get jobs building the necessary stations. This contract provided steady work, but the construction needs slowly moved farther and farther west from Melrose. We didn't realize it at the time, but this would have a huge impact on our family's future.

Father's friendship with two of the leading businessmen in Melrose also led to a number of jobs. W. J. Bohmer and John Borgerding were successful businessmen and deeply involved with the growth of Melrose. Mr. Bohmer was the most important banker in town and became Father's connection for building loans. Mr. Borgerding was involved in banking, but also lumber. He became Father's main source of wood for his contracts. Near the end of the century both men started branching out their interests, investing in new stores and businesses. When Mr. Bohmer wanted to build the W. O. P. Hilsdale brick office building on Main Street in Sauk Centre he called on "E.C. Richmond – Contractor" to complete the task.

When Mr. Bohmer and Mr. Borgerding wanted to build a summer resort on Big Birch Lake north of Melrose, Father got the job. It was a profitable partnership for all concerned, but also brought increased commerce and development to Melrose.

His building success and connections in the area also won him a political appointment as a federal timber estimator. This was a huge honor and brought in extra money, but the biggest advantage was it allowed him to select the best trees and lumber for his own use.

The other change for "E. C. Richmond – Contractor" was bidding on the construction of new, large, regional churches. His success building schools and office buildings led to larger contracts. As his experience grew he was involved in a number of jobs, most notably building St. Paul's Church in Sauk Centre. Most of these jobs had been to build additions, or rebuild older buildings, but by 1898, Father started winning bids to build completely new churches. Not only small, wooden, rural churches, but large, neo-Romanesque churches to dominate the countryside and become the pride of the congregation. The catalyst to Father's expanding role was his successful building of the Church of St. Boniface in Melrose.

By the 1890s the German population in Sterns County, and especially Melrose, had grown considerably. The first German immigrants to come to Minnesota in the 1880s sent letters home to friends and church members encouraging them to move to central Minnesota. They commented on the rich, inexpensive farmland, the climate similar to central Europe, and the political freedoms of America. The unification of Germany under the Protestant prime minister Otto von Bismarck led to new laws and discrimination against German

19

Catholics, most of who lived in the southern parts of the country. This created a large increase in German immigration to the United States, and Minnesota became a popular area to settle. Near the turn of the century Sterns County had one of the largest per capita concentrations of German immigrants in the country. These settlers wanted to speak, read, and worship in their native language. Sterns County had villages named "New Munich," "New Ulm," "Berlin," and "New Trier." German was the native language of much of the county's population and many of the towns in the county had German language newspapers. Many of my friends spoke German and I learned their language as well as English in my youth.

The railroad boom of the 1880s also brought many Irish immigrants to town to work for the Great Northern. The Irish Catholic settlers built St. Patrick's Church in Melrose, but the German Catholics and Irish Catholics had different interpretations of doctrine and different traditions. The German populous wanted services and confession done in their native language. They wanted a church of their own to rival St. Patrick's. The German's worshiped at St. Boniface Church, but it was a small, wooden structure. By the late 1890s the German parish decided to build a grand church to reflect the pride of the German community.

The first foundation stones of St. Cloud granite were cut by the stonemasons of the Melrose Granite Company and moved into place by volunteer parishioners in 1897. Soon after the diocese started accepting bids for the construction of their church. The German-American George Bergmann was the architect and he was heavily influenced by the churches he had seen in his native Bavaria. There were other contractors for the foundation and brickwork, but Father won the bid to be the general contractor in charge of erecting the superstructure. The day the bids were announced he came bursting through the door to tell Mother the news.

"I got it. I got the church. Oh Belle, it's going to be so beautiful. I can't wait to get started."

Mother was always able to bring Father back to reality, but I could tell she was excited too. "Congratulations, Edmond," she said. "This will be a big job and I know you are up to it."

"I'm up to it all right," Father bragged. "I'm the best contractor for this job. That's why I got the contract. This will be wonderful. It will be a landmark here for years and my name will always be attached to it. It could last a hundred years. And, as a sideline, I also won the contract to make the pews. It's worth another fifteen hundred dollars. I'll work on those at my shop while the crew is building the church."

On May 1, 1898, Bishop Trobec came to Melrose to lay the cornerstone for the church. It was an exciting day as the town gathered to witness the event. Our entire family, including Grandmothers Richmond and Conner, were on hand for the ceremony.

Father got to work right away and worked long hours on St. Boniface. He woke early and was at the job site before the sun came up. He hired extra laborers and oversaw their work throughout the day. At night he returned to his carpentry shop to work on the pews and woodwork for the interior. The *Melrose Beacon* reported:

> *Ed Richmond ... is pushing the work as rapidly as possible, overseeing everything personally, and no pains or expense will be spared to fill his contract to the letter and when the structure is finished it will stand out a lasting monument to his*

ability... Every board is finished in his planing mill, one of the bee hives of Melrose, and nothing is done about the building but undergoes his inspection.

For almost a year, if Mama and I wanted to see Father, we went to the building site because he was always there.

On Saturday, October 28, 1898, disaster struck. As the *St. Paul Times* reported, "One of the worst fires of many years occurred [in Melrose] and as a result the planing mill of E. C. Richmond is a total loss." The fire burned uncontrolled for over two hours and everything inside – including the pews for St. Boniface Father was making – was destroyed. The origin of the fire was never discovered, but the loss was well over $30,000.

The entire city of Melrose tried to put out the fire, but it was too big and too hot. A stiff wind blew hot embers all over town and it was all the fire department could do to keep the neighboring buildings from going up in flames. There was nothing we could do except watch as sixteen years of my father's life went up in smoke.

Father was too shocked to discuss anything at the scene of the fire, but later he spoke to my mother.

"I can't believe it's all gone, Belle. My whole life was in that shop. There is no insurance and it will cost thousands and thousands to rebuild. I'm broke. There is nothing in the bank and I can't even pay the mortgage on this house right now.

"Even the pews are gone. I'd spent so much time on them, making them perfect. I was so proud of the work – I couldn't wait to put them in place. It's all gone. What are we going to do? I'm ruined." He couldn't stop talking about it and Mother just let him talk it out.

Finally, after listening to Father's lamentations, Mother calmly said, "Edmond, get yourself together. Let's think this through. You still have the contract for St. Boniface. You have other contracts for building around the county. You can get an advance on those jobs and rebuild. You've always prided yourself on accepting all challenges and winning the bet. This might be your biggest challenge yet. You've never given up on anything in your life, and I don't expect you to give up now. We can start getting loans and workers around tomorrow. You have good contacts in the area. You could see the whole town of Melrose was behind you today at the fire. I'm sure they will help."

Father was quiet for a few minutes thinking about what Mother said. "You are right, Belle. I can overcome this. I've got to look ahead. We will rebuild and it will be bigger and better than before. I can get the most modern woodworking equipment. Yes – we will be positive and turn this disaster into a good thing for both us and Melrose."

Father's competitive side came out and he was determined to rebuild better than ever. The next day Father started contacting everyone he knew and within days he had fifteen prominent businessmen pledging to support his rebuilding effort. The *Melrose Beacon*, who was supporting his rebuilding effort, reported "Though Mr. Richmond is almost crushed by his heavy loss; he is not the man to lay down and give up in despair." It encouraged community support for the rebuilding by saying, "Every man in the city should do what he can toward rebuilding it ... [because] it would show enterprise and prove to the world that the people of Melrose wear hearts and not leather medals."

His plans were for the most modern planing mill in Minnesota. He became obsessed with rebuilding as quickly as possible and worked long hours, six days a week, to get things back in operation.

Within a few weeks the Melrose papers were reporting Father was rebuilding and was making room for a new fifteen-horsepower engine. Less than two months after it was destroyed, Father had his mill back in operation. "E. C. Richmond started his planing mill this week and he seems to be busy every day," reported the newspaper. A few days later they reported his mill "has been compelled to run overtime for the past month or six weeks to keep up with its orders."

Due to his hard work and the support of the community the construction of St. Boniface went on with only minimum delays. It was finished in June 1899, just a little over a year after Father was awarded the contract. Bishop Trobec returned to consecrate the building and lead the first Mass, with over a thousand people attending – even standing in the aisles.

St. Boniface Church was immediately recognized for its size and beauty. It was the largest church in Sterns County. The main building was one hundred eighty feet long, seventy feet wide, and thirty-seven feet high, but the most outstanding features were the twin steeples towering one hundred thirty feet above the city and visible for miles. The steeples were topped with Bavarian style onion domes, announcing to the world the German origin of the congregation. The hand carved high altar was shipped all the way from Germany. It was built with native Minnesota stone and red brick, had a huge nave, and beautiful stained glass windows. The pews, which Father finished in his new workshop, would seat one thousand people. It was the pride of the community.

I beamed with pride when the bishop recognized "Mr. Edmond C. Richmond" during the consecration ceremony. For the rest of his life Father considered St. Boniface his favorite building and his masterpiece.

Thereafter Father's reputation for constructing fine churches brought him numerous opportunities. Within the next year he was awarded the contract to build the Church of St. Bridget in De Graff, Minnesota. This, too, was built in the Romanesque style and was over a hundred feet long and fifty feet wide with a red brick exterior. Father also had the contract for the interior, which had a beautiful, ornate, oak altar and exposed wooden beams. Its steeple was three stories high and could be seen throughout the county. As with his other churches, it was a sensation when completed in 1901.

His other masterpiece was the construction of the first public school in Melrose. While president of the city council he had supported the construction of a new school, but did not want it built until he was out of office so he could bid on the job. Finally, in 1902, the city council approved the idea and granted the bid to Father's construction firm. It was completed the next year. It was a beautiful, three-story, brick structure with six general classrooms, one high school room, a recitation room, a laboratory, a gymnasium, and all the modern conveniences. It even had indoor toilets and running water. You can imagine how proud I was to attend the school my father built.

My life in Melrose seemed complete. Father was a successful businessman, civic leader, and respected throughout the area. Mother was a social leader among the Melrose women, an officer for many civic organizations, and a loving wife and mother. Although I was an only child without many playmates, I never wanted for anything, was well educated, and believed my life in Melrose was secure.

Havre Land Office

"Excuse me, young lady." The man behind me asked a question.

"Oh, I'm sorry. Did you say something?" I asked with some embarrassment. "I've been daydreaming about growing up in Minnesota."

"Minnesota, huh? I'm from Illinois myself. Name's Elmer. Elmer Slonaker. Guess we might as well get to know each other. Montana is a lot different, isn't it? So are you gonna be the one filing the claim, or are you holding the spot for the gentleman who was here earlier?"

Eventually, Elmer Slonaker and his wife, Bessie, would become my closest neighbors and friends, but right now we were just making conversation. "I'm the one filing the claim. My father was here earlier, but it is going to be in my name. I'm excited to have a piece of land all my own."

He looked at me with a bit of a smile. "All by your lonesome? A young woman like you out there all by yourself? You don't look big enough to handle one plow horse, let alone a whole team."

"First of all, call me Mabel," I laughed. "I'm twenty-two and single. My father has a construction contract with the Great Northern. We moved west from Minnesota to North

Dakota and then to Montana always following his next job. I've always lived at home, but I'm ready to get out on my own. It seems someone in the Richmond family has always moved west and settled a claim to some land. I think I've inherited my family's love of adventure. I like a challenge and excitement, and I'm not afraid of hard work. Settling a homestead will allow me to stay close to my parents, but also be part of the growing spirit of this country. It seems to be a passion I have. There are lots of single women homesteading in Montana. I won't be the first, or the last, I'm sure."

"Well, if there are other single women out there, I don't know where. They sure aren't in this here line. Just you," Elmer said. "And you should know, farmin' out here in the dry lands of Montana ain't nothin' like farmin' back in Minnesota. Good luck."

"I've never really farmed, but I've read a lot and think I can handle it. I'll have help from my parents and friends," I continued. "I've been here in Montana for a couple years and I've grown to love the place. The prairie grows on you."

Elmer chuckled, "Well, I know they say the crops grow without any work here in Montana, but I don't believe all that bunk. It's going to be more work than you think."

It was exciting to be number one in front of hundreds of men. I enjoyed waiting and talking to everyone. I had a chair to sit in and my friends in town provided me food and treats. The men behind me became more sociable, talked, and asked questions. Many of them teased me about being the only woman, having a chair, and food – which I shared with the men close to me. We all realized nothing was going to happen until the land office opened, so we might as well be friends. I discovered a vast collection of occupations in line. There were ranchers and farmers, of course, but also lawyers, college

students, single men, married men, runaways, land speculators, and many others. We would all be neighbors within a few
weeks.

As we were talking, Mother walked up and said, "I'll
hold the spot for a while. Your father wants to talk to you."

I found Papa waiting outside on the sidewalk. We
walked through town and he explained how he got the coveted
number one position.

"I was on the train Sunday night, coming back to Havre
from my business trip. You know where the land is we want to
claim? Remember it's the only place around with an irrigation
reservoir. Well, the train was crowded with land seekers and
they were all talking. I overheard two men discussing the land
rush."

The first man said, "We will never get a room in Havre
tonight. Let's go to the Land Office and be first in line."

The other man answered, "Good idea. I've got my claim
all picked out. It's got an irrigation dam on it holding back
almost a hundred acres of water. I can tie up the best piece of
irrigated land in the state. It's up north in Section thirty-five of
Township thirty-six. It will be a great spot."

"I immediately knew he was talking about our spot,"
said Father. "I knew what I had to do. I knew Clem Bougher-
man, the brakeman on the train. I went to Clem and slipped
him ten dollars to let me jump off the train before it stopped. I
was halfway to the Land Office before those guys even got off
the train.

"That's how I got to be first in line, but I wouldn't tell
any of the men. They're likely to be upset if they learn I paid
off the brakeman. So hold on to our spot and we'll get the land
we want."

We knew whoever owned the land with the reservoir would have control of the water in the immediate area. Papa and I were passionate about getting the land when it opened up. It looked like his luck overhearing the two travelers would pay off.

I went back and joined Mother and continued chatting with the men in line. Someone a few spots back looked at Mother and asked, "I hear you've lived here in Havre for a couple years. After I get my claim, I'm going to send for my wife. What should I tell her about the place from a woman's perspective?"

"Tell her to be prepared for anything," said Mother. I was a bit surprised to hear how quickly she answered the question since she was generally standoffish around strangers. "Havre is nice. It is growing fast and has just about anything you could want. If it's not here now, it will be soon. But when you get out of town you have to get used to the isolation and the bleakness of the Plains. I don't know where you're from, but coming from Minnesota, it was a huge shock. I grew up with trees, plenty of water, and many communities within a short distance of each other. Friends and relatives lived a short distance from our home in Melrose and I could visit whenever I wanted.

"We moved to Grand Forks, North Dakota, before we came here. Mabel and I didn't want to move, but Grand Forks wasn't bad. We could return to Melrose and visit our friends with an easy train ride. But out here, everything is a long, long ways away."

Mother continued. I was surprised at her candor. "In Melrose, I had a name in the community. I was proud of my family heritage in the area. I had grown up there and lived there over forty-six years. We lived a prosperous life, Mabel had a good education, Edmond and I were members of the Masons and the Eastern Star, we were leaders in the church, Edmond was a political leader in town, and I loved the entertainment opportunities."

"So why did you leave?" asked one of the other men.

Mother looked at me, then back at the men. "I don't know. My husband is a restless soul. We could have stayed in Melrose, but I'm sure he would not have been satisfied knowing there was something out there he might have missed. Trust me, it wasn't easy to leave. We had many discussions about it and I was insistent on staying. But I realized he would not be happy and it's my job to keep him happy. After almost forty years of marriage, I had to go with him.

"I made him promise Grand Forks would be our last move and we could settle down there. It was okay for a while. Mabel graduated from high school and took classes at the University of North Dakota. We had a nice house in town. But then he started getting jobs in Montana, and pretty soon he came home talking about Montana."

I looked at Mama. We both were thinking of when we left Melrose.

Leaving Melrose

In 1887, Grand Forks, North Dakota, was struck by a huge tornado. Over twenty-five major buildings were damaged, including the Catholic Church and the main building of the University of North Dakota. Hundreds of private homes were damaged, but the citizens were determined to stay put. My father, always looking for an opportunity, took the train to Grand Forks and found the entire city needed to be rebuilt from the ground up. The path of destruction was over a mile long. He quickly started taking jobs. At first, most were simple home constructions, so he could travel back and forth from Melrose to check their progress. But by 1895 he had an office in Grand Forks and had hired a regular work crew. The jobs were easy and very profitable.

Throughout the 1890s Father traveled extensively to building sites in northwestern Minnesota and eastern North Dakota. He was getting more and more jobs in Grand Forks, as the community grew to over five thousand by 1900. I was much too young to realize what was going on. I only remember enjoying the reunions when Papa came home.

Not only Grand Forks, but the entire territory of North Dakota was becoming the destination of homesteaders and immigrants. The cheap, rich, farmland attracted thousands of new settlers. The Great Northern had completed its east-west line across the state by 1900 and started building new lines running north to Canada. These would provide cheap transportation for Canadian grain to the grain mills in Minneapolis and the population of the eastern United States. New communities were springing up all along the Great Northern line and its spurs north and south. Father wanted to get in on the growth and started speculating on both land and city growth.

W. J. Bohmer also saw the potential for riches in North Dakota. By 1902 Father and Mr. Bohmer had formed an agreement to invest in the new railroad towns of Osnabrock and Sarles. Both cities were northwest of Grand Forks near the Canadian border and E. C. Richmond got the contracts to build banks for W. J. Bohmer and stations for the Great Northern.

Father came home after a trip to those sites and explained his enthusiasm to Mother. "Belle, I want to buy some land in North Dakota. I think it's a good risk and an investment for the future. W. J. Bohmer is expanding his banking and business interests into North Dakota. The towns of Osnabrock and Sarles are on new spurs of the Great Northern running north into Canada. Bohmer and I both agree they have great potential to become trade centers with Canada. The farmers on the Canadian plains can ship their grain to market from there easier than from Winnipeg. Bohmer wants me to build a bank for him and a new brick store in Osnabrock. Then we will do the same in Sarles. You know I trust W. J. and owe him a lot. It's an exciting opportunity and I don't want to be left out of the growth."

So Father started taking more jobs in North Dakota. He continued to get jobs in the Melrose area, such as the Melrose school, churches in neighboring communities, and private residences. He would travel to North Dakota for a week or two to inspect and supervise construction jobs there, then return to Melrose to see us and conduct business at home. It was a hectic, busy schedule but he seemed to thrive on it. In the meantime, Mother and I continued with my schooling and our social activities. Occasionally in the summer, we would travel to North Dakota and stay with Father.

By 1904, the extensive traveling and time away from family and friends started to wear on him. One night he came home and told Mother and me to join him in the parlor. He was very stern and direct – more than usual.

"Belle, you're not going to like this, but we've got to move to Grand Forks. I can't carry on like this, and there are too many business opportunities in North Dakota to pass up. They are growing much more than Melrose and I'm getting jobs faster than I can complete them."

"No!" shouted Mother emphatically. "I'm not leaving Melrose. I grew up here. My parents and siblings are here. Everything I've ever wanted is here. I've been to Grand Forks with you. Mabel and I even visited you in Sarles last year and stayed for two weeks. We've seen the barren wasteland they call the prairie. There's not a tree in sight and it's so isolated. No – I'm not going."

Father was sympathetic, but his mind was made up. "I don't want to do it either, but I have to. I grew up here, too. I know everyone in town. I'm a community leader and an officer in the local Masons. But I have built just about everything possible in the county – schools, office buildings, stores, and churches – and things are getting stagnant."

"So, aren't you happy here?" Mother asked.

Father paused for a moment and reflected. He had thought this through for a long time. "I suppose the average guy would be happy, but I am over fifty and restless. I have never been able to stay still. I've always traveled around. I like to hunt, fish, and be outside. You know I love you and Mabel, but I have never been able to stay home very long. I'm an entrepreneur who wants to succeed. I look at Grand Forks and see great opportunities and more money. I'm not afraid to start over in a new place."

"Well, I'm not leaving," said Mother defiantly. "You go to North Dakota and come home when you can. Mabel and I will visit and see if we like it there. Let's see what develops and how good business is in another year. In the meantime, we will try to continue as normal as possible here in Melrose. We will talk about this later." Mother was patient and practical, but she could be very stubborn. She was not going to agree with Papa without a fight, and he knew it. He knew she would not move if she did not have to. So for the next year, Father lived in Grand Forks, came home when he could, and we visited every couple months. In the meantime, neither parent asked for my opinion.

Although Grand Forks remained Father's center of operation, his construction jobs and various business ventures took him farther and farther west in North Dakota. Soon he was building north of Minot. He bought a 480-acre farm in north-central North Dakota intending to rent it out for a profit. He had it plowed and advertised for a tenant farmer to run it, but land was cheap and new settlers weren't interested in running someone else's farm. It was never rented and ultimately returned to grasslands.

Mother and I would visit Father in North Dakota in the summer and fall, even attending a ball at the new Sarles Hotel. The first train trips to Grand Forks and the prairie were adventures. The trip took all day, with stops in Sauk Centre,

Evanston, Fergus Falls, and Fargo before pulling into Grand Forks. From Grand Forks it took another six hours to get to Sarles. I excelled in science and always liked geography so the changing scenery fascinated me. We went from the rolling hills and forests around Melrose, past the lakes of northwestern Minnesota, and into the prairie of North Dakota.

Grand Forks was a rapidly growing community. I could understand Father's excitement. It was an important trade center. The Red River, flowing north, provided easy transportation with Canada and the Great Northern Railroad, which had been there since the 1880s, connected it to the east and west. Immigrants from Germany and Scandinavia poured into the area with the promise of cheap land and the rail lines provided an easy route to ship grains from the prairie to the mills in Minneapolis and Chicago.

In the spring of 1905 Mother and I made another trip to Grand Forks. Mother was still hesitant to leave Melrose. I was fifteen and attending Melrose High School. I had my first crush on a young man in class and didn't want to leave either. We both knew Father had been very busy and had received many contracts in North Dakota, but we still didn't want to accept the inevitable.

Father greeted us at the station and took us to the apartment he was renting. Along the way, he went by a bank building under construction.

"What do you think?" he asked as he pointed out a sign announcing "E. C. Richmond Construction" was building the bank. "It's the first of many banks I am contracted to build. If I make my bids right, I could have a contract with the Beecher-Felton combination to build six or seven banks over the next year."

"It looks very nice," said Mother stoically. "I imagine building so many banks will keep you busy here in Grand Forks. Any idea when you might get back to Melrose?"

"That's just it, Belle. I don't see any chance of getting back to Melrose and I want you and Mabel here with me. I need my family near. You are always a huge help in keeping me focused on work and responsibilities."

Father looked at me, hoping for another opinion. "What do you think Mabel? Grand Forks is a much bigger city. It has new shops and a bigger school. When you finish high school you can attend the University of North Dakota right here and not even have to leave home. Doesn't that sound more exciting than staying in Melrose?" Father was doing his best to make it appealing to me.

"I can't leave Melrose Papa." I blurted out. "I love it there and want to stay. I think Grand Forks is a lovely city and it is much larger and more exciting than Melrose, but all my friends are back home. And there are no trees here – I love to walk in the woods and enjoy the colors of the trees in the fall. I can't leave Melrose."

The tone was set for the rest of the visit. Father tried desperately to convince us Grand Forks was a better place to live than Melrose. He took us on boat rides down the Red River. He took us to the best shops and spent time with us, which was very unusual for him. We went to the opera at the Grand Forks Metropolitan Opera House, which considered the finest facility west of the Mississippi. Although we were sure Father wasn't interested in opera and only went to please us, Mother and I loved the performance of *The Pirates of Penzance*. After the opera he showed us a house he wanted to buy. Nothing could change Mother's mind though, and when we left two weeks later, we were still at an impasse. We would continue to live in Melrose, and Father would visit when he could.

Mother's stoic attitude broke down on the train ride home. "Mabel, now that we are by ourselves, what did you really think of Grand Forks?"

I gave Mother a quizzical look. "What are you saying? Are you thinking of moving?" I was surprised by the question and caught off guard. I thought for a moment. "Grand Forks wasn't bad. It did have some nice stores, and I loved the opera at the Metropolitan. If we lived there I could go to the university, which you have been encouraging. I'm not sure why you're asking. The whole time we were Grand Forks you were dead set against moving."

Mother looked at me and smiled. "You are right. I told Edmond I wouldn't move, and probably made him miserable with my stubbornness, but I do hate being apart from him. He has a number of great job opportunities in Grand Forks. I've been involved in his business dealings and have to agree there is not much more he can do in Melrose. And he has to keep working. If he stopped, it would kill him. I can't think of many reasons not to move to Grand Forks. We can take the train back to Melrose if we want to visit family. North Dakota is not as ugly as we made it sound – the prairie is actually growing on me a little. I'm thinking we will have to give in eventually, so this might be the right time. I've always said – don't resist change, accept it."

I was torn. "I'm not sure how to answer. I love Melrose, and I'd hate to leave my friends – especially this one boy I like. But it is rather exciting to think about moving. I love new places and new adventures, and Grand Forks would definitely be a new adventure. Can we think about it and talk about it some more?"

"Yes," Mother calmly replied. "We won't say anything to anyone yet. We will make this our little secret and see how this year goes. If Father is successful in getting his bids and the related work, we will look at next summer to move. If something happens and he doesn't get the work, we will stay in Melrose and no one will be the wiser."

"Yes, Mama," I replied. "I like that plan." It was settled.

Upon our return to Melrose it seemed everyone wanted to know about our trip to North Dakota and what our future plans were. According to plan, we told everyone we were staying in Melrose. Even the society column in the *Melrose Beacon* reported, "they enjoyed their stay in North Dakota, [but] will not make that state their home as many of their friends feared." When Father came home a few weeks after us, it seemed to calm everyone's concerns. I was overwhelmed by the concern of our friends and felt bad denying anything about North Dakota, but it had to be done. We had no idea what the rest of the year would bring.

Mabel circa 1906

By the spring of 1906 there was no denying the inevitable. Father came back to Melrose in March for a short break from work to talk to us.

"Belle, this isn't working. I cannot go on like this with you and Mabel here in Melrose and me in Grand Forks. I am busier than ever. I have more jobs than I've ever had in Minnesota. Last year I built eight banks and I'm contracted to build nine more this year. My contract to build stations for the Great Northern is taking me farther west. And the business ventures in Osnabrock and Sarles look promising. The villages are growing and if trade continues they will be important in the future. Those places are a day's ride from Grand Forks and I can't monitor their construction if I'm here in Melrose. There aren't any more interesting jobs here. Will you please reconsider and move to Grand Forks?"

Mother looked at me and smiled, "Yes – we will move. Mabel and I have been watching you work and realized a few months ago we would probably have to move. It's not going to be easy to leave, but I agree we have to do it."

Papa looked at me and I nodded in agreement. I wanted to be part of the conversation. "I only have two requests."

"And what would those be little lady?" Father was suddenly in a much better mood. He hadn't expected the decision to be so easy.

"I want a house big enough to have a piano. And I want to be able to continue my education at the university after I leave high school."

"That's easy," said Papa. "I already have a house picked out, and going to the university is up to you."

Once we decided to move, everything fell in place quickly. In March Father sold the machinery in his planing and sash mill and dissolved the business. In April I had my sixteenth birthday. My friends Beth, Anna, and Gertrude had a wonderful party for me and invited all my classmates. They gave me a beautiful broach as a going away gift. We laughed and cried most of the afternoon. Then, on the first of May, the Masons and women of the Eastern Star had a ball in honor of my father and mother's service to the community. Many regional dignitaries attended including the mayor of Sauk Centre and a representative from the state capital. They even read a telegram from Father's childhood friend and neighbor, Charles August Lindbergh, who was running for election to the House of Representatives. Lindbergh thanked Father for his friendship and service to the community. It was a gala evening with many toasts and compliments.

We kept the house in Melrose as our permanent address, but rented it to a new resident. We promised everyone we would be back, especially in the summer. But I would be going to school in Grand Forks and we would have a house there, so it seemed to be an empty promise, or maybe a wish to return to keep everyone happy.

We left Melrose on June 1, 1906. Grandmothers Richmond and Conner, along with many other relatives and friends, accompanied us to the station where we said our good-byes. We promised to return for visits and vacations, but it was a hard day for all of us. It was a day of love, hugs, and lots of tears. As the train pulled away, I buried my face to hide my tears. Father gave me a stern look of disapproval and said, "Mabel, you must hold your head up like a lady. Look to the future and grasp the opportunities in front of you."

Mother's words were spoken softer, with a gentle smile. "Yes dear, you have to realize life is like a good book. It is a series of chapters, all leading to the grand conclusion. And like a good book, you have to anticipate what is coming in the next chapter. You may briefly look back at a previous chapter to remember something, but you've already been there so you want to look ahead. Turn the page." It was so simple when she said it, and it made sense. I determined I would not look back and looked forward to the next chapter with excitement.

Grand Forks: 1906-1910

Father had everything ready when we arrived in Grand Forks. A carriage picked us up at the station and gave us on a leisurely ride through town. After a while we stopped in front of a lovely little house at 212 Chestnut Street. This was our new home. Father had bought it as soon as we agreed to move. Mother and I were surprised the house was ready for us. I jumped out of the carriage and ran to the front door. Father insisted on escorting us through, but I could not hold back my excitement and ran into the house. There, in the front room, over in a corner by itself, was a new upright piano.

"Papa – I love it!" I squealed. "You kept your promise. I didn't expect it to be here when we moved in. Oh – it is beautiful. Thank you, thank you, thank you!" I gave him a big kiss.

Father smiled, "Anything for my little girl."

I started to play my favorite tunes – Scott Joplin ragtime. Father and Mother usually disliked ragtime, but they smiled at each other and proceeded to inspect the rest of the house. I didn't need to see anything else.

Grand Forks was exciting for a young lady. The population was more diverse than Melrose. Farmers, businessmen, traders, trappers, river men, lawyers, and university professors all worked and shopped in the city by the Red River.

Canadians, easterners, and southerners all mingled together. Immigrants from Europe – especially from Germany, Scandinavia, and Russia – got off the train every day looking for opportunities in one of the fastest growing communities in the north-central plains. Land was cheap, plentiful, and attractive to many. Even Indians from the plains came to town regularly. It was a mix of people and cultures I had not experienced.

Father had already joined the local Masons and Mother quickly became active in various ladies' organizations, the Eastern Star, and the local Episcopal Church. In the fall I enrolled in Grand Forks High School. I discovered it was easy to make friends. Grand Forks was a new community and had many new residents. Everyone at school wanted to make new friends. I became part of student government and was on the girls' basketball team. I loved the game and the chance to be competitive. We won three games my junior year and six my senior year.

Father's construction business took off. His bank projects kept him busy throughout the year and he received more contracts from the railroad to build stations. He also had some projects back in Minnesota requiring his presence. As a result, he was gone on business as much as he was the year before.

In the spring of 1907 I had a new love interest. Theodore Losbrock, a tall, blond senior with penetrating blue eyes, was in my Latin class. He was a star athlete on the high school basketball and baseball teams. We talked often at school and he wanted to take me to the Spring Ball. He walked me home one day after school in order to meet my father and ask his permission.

Theodore was nervous, and I tried to reassure him, "My father will be gruff and stern, but don't let him scare you. He's really quite a softy once you get to know him. Just be polite and patient. I doubt he will say 'yes' right away."

"Father – Mother – would you come here please?" I called when we arrived at the house. "I have someone I'd like you to meet."

My parents came into the foyer and I introduced them to Theodore.

"Good evening Mr. and Mrs. Richmond," Theodore stuttered. "Pleased to meet you."

"Good evening Mister Losbrock," Father took on the stern, domineering look I had expected. Father, never being one for small talk, got right to the point. "And for what do we have the pleasure of this meeting?"

Even though I had tried to warn him, Theodore was taken aback by Father's manner. "Well sir, I uh, what I want to ask is ... Excuse me." He coughed loudly, cleared his throat, gathered up his courage and blurted out, "I would like your permission to escort Mabel to the Spring Ball."

"Thank you for asking, but the answer is no," stated Father bluntly.

"Papa – how can you answer so quickly?" I interjected. I had tried to stay discreet and not say anything, but Father's rude answer shocked me. "You've hardly heard him out."

"Mabel – you are much too young to go to a school dance without a chaperone. I won't have my only daughter out late at night with a young man whom I hardly know. Thank you for asking Theodore, but the answer is still no."

I was aghast at his answer. "Papa – I'm seventeen. I've been singing and playing piano in church and theater since I was six. I have been with you and Mother at numerous dances and balls. You know how much I love music and dancing.

Theodore is an outstanding student and a well known athlete. You can trust us."

"No – and don't question me again."

Theodore was lost in this argument and wasn't quite sure what to say. Finally he said, "I'd better be going. Nice to meet you Mr. and Mrs. Richmond." He turned and left quickly.

After he was gone, Mother spoke up. "Edmond – you know I will never contradict you in public. I wasn't going to say anything with the young man here, but I think it's time you let Mabel go out on her own. Remember, I was only seventeen when we got married. She's our only daughter, but you can't shelter her forever."

"What are you saying, Belle?"

Mother was the only person I knew who could stand up to Father. She would stand right in front of him with her tiny frame and look straight up at him. She spoke softly, but directly, and said what she felt. Father rarely withstood her arguments without giving in.

"I'm saying it's time we let Mabel go to the ball with an escort. I trust her. When you are out of town on business it's just the two of us here. You have no idea how much independence she has when you aren't around. She shops on her own and takes care of many things around the house for me. She has much more freedom when you aren't here than you are aware of."

Father looked at me, then looked at Mother. I knew he would give in, but he wasn't about to let Mother win easily. "Let me think about it for awhile. I want to know more about the boy and the dance. And I'm going to make sure you are home very early young lady."

The next day Father approved of Theodore. I thanked Mother for standing up for me. Without her, I never would have experienced the ball. Theodore and I had a lovely time at the Spring Ball, but Theodore and I never went out again. We were still friends, but we had different interests and directions in our lives. He was happy to work on his father's farm after school. I, on the other hand, wanted to continue my education, perform on stage, and play piano in an orchestra.

The next spring, before my eighteenth birthday in April, Father came home very excited. "Belle, Mabel – today is a great day. The Board of Trustees for St. Michael's Parish has awarded me the contract to build their new church. After the old church burned down last September they decided to spare no expense on the replacement. They want the best building possible. It's a huge job. The entire cost will be close to $100,000. My portion alone is going to cost almost $49,000. But I've seen the plans and if I can do this right it will be the biggest, most beautiful church in North Dakota."

"Oh Edmond – that is wonderful," exclaimed Mother. "Who designed it?"

"You've heard of the Hancock brothers. They have designed many of the buildings here in Grand Forks since the big tornado. They are great architects and I'm very excited to work for them. This will really put my name out there. I can't wait to get started.

"We can start on the foundation right away. We will have to wait for the rest of the materials to be delivered from the east. We will need tons of granite and red brick." In his excitement Father couldn't stop talking about it.

Father once again started a demanding, obsessive schedule. He supervised the work crews daily and personally helped with much of the construction. He was always at the work site, even inspecting parts of the job late at night.

He only took one small break from work. He had promised me he would not miss my high school graduation, so on June 3, 1908, he watched thirty-six classmates and I graduate from Grand Forks High School. I sang a cantata with the girls' glee club at the ceremony and saw Father beaming with pride when my name was introduced.

Mother hosted a reception at the Episcopal Church in honor of the graduates. When I arrived I was surprised to see a photograph of me predominantly displayed at the entrance. It had been taken only a week before, but I had not seen it. It was a portrait of me in a white lace blouse, high collar, with the alabaster broach my friends in Melrose had given me pinned at my neck. The white background accented my dark hair done in a Pompadour - the "Gibson Girl" look was the fashion of the day. I had a distant look in my eye because the photographer asked me to dream of where I was going to be in the next five years. Everyone who came to the reception commented on the photograph.

Mabel's high school graduation picture

"Mabel – this is a stunning picture of you. You look marvelous," said Mrs. Cary. More important to me was the person standing next to her. Her son, Burton, looked at the picture, then looked at me sheepishly, and agreed, "Yes, it is a very nice picture, Mabel." He smiled at me as he walked away with his mother. Burton and I had been talking at school, but he had never expressed anything more than a friendly interest. However, by the end of the night he had spoken to my father and asked to take me to the Masonic Temple's dance the following week. We had a wonderful time at the dance but did not see each other afterward.

During the summer, after my graduation festivities were complete, Mother and I returned to Melrose for an extended stay. We had returned occasionally for the last two years, but those were only short visits with relatives and friends. This stay was for two months, which was time for us to enjoy the Melrose social scene again, boat and swim at Big Birch Lake, and renew our connection to the city. Father came and went, with various construction projects in the area. When he was in town he would often talk up the beauty and riches of the western plains. When we left in September the *Melrose Beacon* even reported that "after spending a pleasant summer here, Miss Richmond will enter North Dakota University at Great Falls this year."

By October 1908 most of the outside walls of St. Michael's were completed, the pipe organ was delivered, and work was started on the altar. In December, less than eight months after first being awarded the contract, the basement of St. Michael's was completed and the congregation was able to celebrate their first Mass. For the last year the parishioners had been meeting in the roller rink and office buildings to hold services. There was still much work to be done, but everyone was excited to worship in their own building.

Father's obsessive focus on building St. Michael's often made him absent-minded and oblivious to the day-to-day activities going on around him. One evening in July there was a knock on the door. Father answered and a young man who introduced himself as James McLoughlin greeted him.

Father recognized the name. "Are you the son of Judge McLoughlin?"

"Yes sir," he replied. "I believe I have found your wallet."

Father looked bewildered for a moment, and then realized he had not seen his wallet all day. "Why, I've been so busy I didn't even know I had misplaced it. Are you sure it's mine? Where did you find it?"

"I found it on Sixth Street, near the St. Michael's construction site, and I'm sure it's yours, sir. I looked inside and found your business card. Here it is," and he pulled Father's business card out of the wallet.

"There must be over five hundred dollars there," exclaimed Father. "I received a payment yesterday and have not had time to get to the bank yet. Is it all there?"

Young Mr. McLoughlin looked nervous. "Yes sir. I counted it. There is $515. It's all there."

"You are a wonderfully honest young man." Father took the wallet, looked around like he was not quite sure what to do, then pulled out a dollar bill. "I want to reward you for your honesty. We need more young men like you around. Here take this dollar as my thank you."

Mr. McLoughlin awkwardly took the bill. "Thank you, sir. I wanted to do what was right. Good night." And he turned around and left.

Mother and I watched all this transpire without saying anything. When Father turned away from the door, Mother looked at him and said, "You only gave him one dollar? Edmond Richmond – you had over five hundred dollars in your wallet and he returned it untouched. You don't think you could have given him more?"

"Goodness no, Belle. We should all be honest without an expectation of reward. I almost didn't give him anything."

Father continued working long hours on St. Michael's, even in the dead of winter, and a year later, October 1909, the church was completed. Since we were not Catholic we would not be attending the special service and Mass, however, Father arranged a private tour for us the day before. Father Conaty, who had been the pastor of St. Michael's for over twenty years, escorted us.

"Edmond," Father Conaty said, "Your crews have been wonderful to work with. Because of your hard work we are able to conduct services less than two years after our old church burned down. And what a structure. I have received compliments from everyone who has seen it. I have heard the gold crosses on the two towers can be seen from over five miles out of town. The red brick with the granite trim, the three large doors covered by rounded arches, and the beautiful rose window are more magnificent than I ever thought they would be. Thank you for your excellent work."

"I'm humbled Father." And for once in his life, I believe my father actually was without words. He smiled and said, "I was not the only contractor. I hope you pass on your compliments to the workers who completed the windows and the artwork inside."

"Oh yes," said Father Conaty. "The interior is also impressive. The altar, statues, and stained glass windows all deserve recognition. And the pipe organ – you should hear the sound ring through the church. It is so full, you can almost feel the music."

I was amazed at the size of the church. I had been in many of Father's buildings, including the churches he built back in Minnesota, but this was by far his best work. Father

49

Conaty took us up in one of the bell towers and we could see forever. Looking north, along the Red River, I felt I could see all the way to Canada. It was an exciting experience and I was so proud of my father for his contribution to this memorable building.

Father's contract with the Great Northern Railroad continued to bring him good jobs and kept his construction crews busy. In the summer of 1909, before St. Michael's was completed, he was awarded the bid to build a new ten-train roundhouse in Grand Forks. He also continued to get contracts to build stations along the Great Northern line. As western North Dakota and eastern Montana opened up for homesteading more and more immigrants and easterners moved into the area. As a result, new communities were popping up along the line and the railroad needed new stations. These jobs were profitable and provided new territory for Father's real estate speculation.

While his construction company continued to get interesting and exciting jobs, like St. Michael's, his work with the Great Northern was important because Father needed a reliable source of income and the railroad provided steady and predictable work. He made plenty of money, but Father always seemed in need of more. He loved buying new things and being the first in town to have something unique. He was always looking for an easy way to make a fortune but unfortunately lost on a number of speculation schemes. Mother tried to rein in his spending, but it was futile and she would eventually give in and accept his spendthrift ways.

While Father worked, Mother and I spent time learning to love Grand Forks. We returned to Melrose a few times for weddings and funerals of relatives and friends, but for the most part we stayed in the area and discovered the joys of eastern North Dakota. Mother continued her community activities, spending a considerable amount of time in activities at the Episcopal Church, the Order of the Eastern Star, and Community Theater. We also became active with the new Young Women's Christian Association in town. The YWCA had many charity events we volunteered for. I continued with my music and art and took roles in the community theater productions.

I learned to love the Plains. The wide, flat Red River Valley had its own special beauty. Much of the land was still dominated by native grasses and wildflowers. Spring was my favorite season. As the winter freeze thawed, the warmer days brought a wild display of color from the grasses and the wildflowers. The purple thistle and phlox, the yellow black-eyed Susan, the blue bachelor buttons and cornflowers contrasted with the light green of the new grass making an ever-changing landscape to enjoy, Mother and I would go for long rides into the prairie in the spring and find new spots to explore.

The long days of summer could be blistering hot, but were usually comfortable for walking along the river, or taking a pleasant boat ride. Autumn had its own character. The temperature was cool and pleasant, and the changing colors provided a dreamy atmosphere. There were not as many trees as in Melrose, but where the trees grew along the river and in town the colors were brilliant.

Winter, of course, was harsh and bitter cold. The wind and snow came out of the north and swept unmolested across the Plains. Winter was when Mother and I would knit, sew, or do needlework. I would play piano for hours at a time. It also was the time for plays, dancing, basketball, and many indoor activities. Mother was an avid card player. She taught me how

to play bridge in Minnesota, but there she had regular partners so I didn't play much. However, when we moved to Grand
Forks I became her favorite partner. I loved the game. We
would go to friends' homes, or to the Masonic Temple and play
bridge for the entire afternoon. We would often play three or
four days a week during the winter.

I enrolled in classes at the University of North Dakota
in the fall of 1908. The school was located less than a mile
from home, so it was easy to attend. First semester I took the
required freshman classes: English, math, history, chemistry,
and civics. Second semester I tried to choose classes I thought
I would enjoy and put to good use: art, music, and German. I
enjoyed the art classes and German came easy because of my
early exposure in Minnesota, but I must admit I wasn't a very
motivated student and my grades – mostly "B's" and "C's" –
reflected my lack of effort. Mother would prod me to do better,
but I was easily distracted by young men and Mother Nature.
The most interesting thing in German class was the presence
of a young man with thick blond hair and big blue eyes. We
became good friends, talked regularly, but never dated. I was
discouraged by my failure to develop a lasting relationship
with any young man in Grand Forks. One evening, while
Father was away on a business trip, I asked Mother about my
lack of male companionship.

Mother was direct, but very tender at the same time.
She looked at me with a sweet smile and said, "Mabel – you
are too smart and independent for most young men. You have
an adventurous streak in you. Most young men today want a
woman who is quiet, demure, and obedient. You haven't been
raised that way. Both your Father and I want you to be intelligent, think for yourself, have opinions, and not be afraid to
express them. We want you to be able to make decisions on

your own. By being a young lady with those characteristics, you scare a lot of men. But when you find a man as independent and adventurous as you – you will have a wonderful match."

"But Mother," I said, "I'm not trying to be like that. I'm not trying to scare the boys. It's just the way I am. I want to make my own decisions and be independent. I want to be a strong woman. I can't imagine being pushed around by a husband or any man and obediently sitting at home and doing nothing. I want to get out and do things."

"Then you'll have to be patient, dear. The right man will come along."

Father's contract with the Great Northern Railroad kept taking him even farther west. The railroads needed small stations every eight to ten miles so trains could pull on to a siding and allow trains to pass in the opposite direction. Father's job was to build these stations and other associated buildings for the railroad. Many of these jobs were in Montana and the work became centered on Havre, Montana. Havre was an important hub and the regional headquarters for the Great Northern. From there trains could continue west across the Rockies to Seattle or south to Great Falls and the mining areas of Helena and Butte.

Consequently, Father established a construction office in Havre and was spending more and more time there. Mother and I weren't surprised when he came home and announced we were moving to Havre.

"I already have a house in town. Havre is booming. A huge fire in 1904 destroyed much of the downtown area, but it is rebuilding and is new and modern. The Great Northern has invested a lot of money in town and is building more headquarters buildings. I have to be there to get the jobs."

Mother knew the outcome of the discussion, but wasn't going to give in without a fight. She wanted to hear Father's justification and logic for the move. "Edmond – we've had this discussion before. Only four years ago, when we left Melrose, you promised us Grand Forks would be our last move. You told us there was enough work to keep you busy the rest of your life. Now you want us to move again? Why?"

"Belle," said Father with a firm, demanding, but still gentle look in his eye, "I'm almost fifty-eight. I need to keep working, but I am no longer interested in building private residences. Constantly looking for new jobs and the bidding wars is exasperating, tiresome, and annoying. This contract with the Great Northern is long lasting, steady, and good money. I can work for them as long as I want. And there is good land in Montana. The government is starting to open up much of the land for settlement. I would like to work long enough to get ahead and settle down as a so-called gentleman farmer. It's great hunting, too. I can see myself doing some ranching and farming in five or six years. Wouldn't it be nice to have a nice spread somewhere and be able to quietly do whatever we want to do? That's what I want."

Mother didn't answer. She remained quiet and looked at me, "Mabel – what do you think?"

"Well, I felt this was going to happen sooner or later. Father has been in Montana a lot recently, and I don't especially like it when he's gone. I love it here. I have made new friendships and enjoy the university and the chance to improve my music and artwork. But I've discovered I like moving and new opportunities. I like the prairie more than I thought I would when we left Melrose. I've thought about it quite a bit in the last couple weeks – I think I'm okay with it. I think Havre sounds like it will be a good place for me to establish myself, get out on my own, and make a name for myself. So – let's go."

It was decided. Another chapter ended and a new one opened up in front of me.

Havre: 1910-1913

As Mother and I reminisced about Melrose and Grand Forks a small group of men gathered around listening to our story. They wanted to know more about our move to Montana. "So have you been happy out here?" one of the men asked.

Mother answered without hesitation, "Some might think this is paradise, but not from this lady's perspective. But I adjust and do what my husband wants. That's the way I was brought up."

"Sometimes you are too much a lady, Mother," I interjected. "I think we were disappointed when we first arrived. We heard great stories about how much we would like it. I remember Father coming home and telling us about the wide-open plains, the mountains in the distance, the Hi-Line, and lots of other stories. Looking out the windows of our Pullman car on the way here was depressing – nothing but flat grasslands for as far as you could see as we came across North Dakota and eastern Montana. A few years ago we could travel to St. Paul and other large cities in a couple of hours, but coming out here we didn't see any signs of civilization for hours at a time. The station stops were tiny little burgs.

"But once we got here and were settled we learned to love the wide-open spaces. We have been here almost three years. Mother and I frequently ride our buggy out into the grasslands to enjoy the view and the fresh air. The scenery is subtle, and mesmerizing. We've learned this is a growing community and we want to be a part of it. We have a comfortable house on Seventh Street. Father has joined the Masons and the Elks. Mother is active in the church, and I have enjoyed taking part in many of the theater and musical activities in town."

"You a musician?" one of the men asked. "I play the accordion myself. I've been wondering if there were any bands around I could join."

"I love music. When Father was trying to convince us to move here he promised to bring my piano from Grand Forks. When we arrived he had the piano already moved to our house. I play every day – classical, religious, or ragtime – I don't care, I just love to play. I've already told Papa I want my piano moved to my new house on the homestead."

"So you're going to be the one living out on the prairie? You make it sound like it's going to be easy. It's going to take a lot of hard, physical work, little lady. It isn't going to be as easy as you make it sound," said the handsome young redhead further back in line. He had been listening to our story without saying anything.

"Hey Red, give her a break," said the man next to him. "She wants to give it a try."

I looked at him and gave him a confident smile. "I'll get by. I'm not as soft as I may appear. I'm ready for the hard work." I turned back to Mother. She nodded in agreement. "She'll be fine. I have confidence in her."

We sat quietly for a while and I thought back to our arrival in Havre.

Father had taken his first trips to Havre in 1907 and by 1908 was getting contracts. Havre was growing rapidly, primarily because of the Great Northern Railroad. The city's population had jumped from two thousand to almost five thousand in less than ten years, creating many opportunities for investors, speculators, and businessmen. Telephone service reached the city in 1908 and the city successfully lobbied for new roads connecting it to Great Falls, Chinook, and Warsaw. It was quickly becoming the hub of north-central Montana.

In early 1909 Father met one of Havre's leading citizens, Mr. Frank A. Buttrey. Mr. Buttrey opened a grocery and dry goods store in Havre in the 1890s, but his store was destroyed in the Great Fire of 1904. He wanted a new, larger, more diverse store – a full-scale department store like nothing else in Montana at the time. Father won the contract to build the new store.

Construction started in late 1909 and by the fall of 1910 the store was complete. The two-story building occupied the entire block between Second and Third streets and was the pride of Havre. It was constructed entirely of steel, brick, and reinforced concrete, which made it virtually fireproof. It had 37,000 square feet of selling space and was the largest mercantile store under one roof in the entire state. The electric lights made it bright as day inside, even after sunset. It had telephones connecting the different floors and departments. It even had elevators. The *Harlem Enterprise* called it "the most modern store erected in Northern Montana".

Father was extremely proud of the finished building. He had successfully built churches which would last a hundred years in Minnesota and North Dakota. Now he had made his mark in Montana. He wanted to ensure Mother and I moved to

Havre before the grand opening in November, so he bought a house on Seventh street and had it ready when we arrived in September. My one demand on the move was to keep my piano. Father shipped it to Havre and it was in the living room when we arrived. The house was small, but comfortable.

Mr. Buttrey had a Grand Opening reception at the department store and, of course, we were invited. Father was one of the guests of honor and we were given a private tour of the store. I had not seen anything like it west of St. Paul. It had everything a person could need: food, clothing, cosmetics, and even furniture and appliances. It was exciting to walk through the different departments.

Since Mother and I had only been in town a few weeks, being in the reception line with Father gave us an opportunity to meet many of the leading citizens of Havre. The mayor and city council, the regional manager of the Great Northern, the leading clergy, and the top investors in the city were all there. But there was one young man who was especially interesting to me. He came through the line with the rest of his family, who had been residents of Havre for some time. He was about five feet, eight inches tall, broad-shouldered, and muscular. He had a full head of thick, dark hair and bright blue eyes that seemed to penetrate right through me. His name was Leo Delorimier.

Later in the evening, when the band started playing, he boldly walked over and asked me to dance. "Miss Richmond, please excuse my directness. You caught my eye as soon as I walked in tonight. I decided I must ask you to dance."

His directness surprised me and caught me off guard, but it also excited me. Proper etiquette would have been for me to refuse until we had been properly introduced and had talked for a few minutes, but I couldn't refuse.

"Thank you Mr. Delorimier," I managed to say. We danced a simple little dance, but I was having a hard time concentrating, as I found myself staring into his blue eyes. "We have only recently arrived in town so it is nice to meet someone my age."

He quietly said, "My family has been here since 1900. If you'd like, I could show you around town and introduce you to some friends."

It wasn't really the proper thing to say, but I blurted out, "I would like that," as we continued our dance. I realized later I probably should have asked Father first, but he had become more permissive in the last few months, so I figured it would be okay. It was.

Leo and I met the next day and walked through downtown Havre. He was twenty-one – only a year older than me – and a second generation French-Canadian. He graduated from Havre High School with honors and played guard on the football team. He worked for the Great Northern and was working his way up. He was personable, confident, and bold. I found him attractive, attentive, and someone I wanted to know better.

As we walked Leo explained the history of the city.

"Havre was founded in the 1890s and named after the French city Le Havre by its French-Canadian settlers. It's what attracted my parents to move here," he explained. "It has grown fast, mainly because of the railroad. The city stretches east and west along the Milk River for about a mile. As you can see the river valley is lined with cottonwood trees, but away from the river valley there is nothing but grassland for as far as you can see. On the western edge of town is a series of cliffs and ravines known locally as the Badlands. Perhaps we can ride up there some day."

"It sounds exciting. I love geography and I'm amazed at the variety of the landscapes around here."

Leo enjoyed impressing me with his local knowledge. "Then we will have to make a trip to the Bear Paw Mountains. Those are the mountains you see to the south. They are only about twenty miles away. The beautiful trees and valleys provide quite a contrast to the surrounding prairie.

"We also have Fort Assinniboine six miles southwest of town. The fort was established to provide a military presence in northern Montana after the Nez Perce and Chief Joseph were defeated at the Battle of Bear Paw in 1877. It is not as important now since most of the Indians have been moved to the reservations, but you will see soldiers from the fort coming into town. In particular, the fort is the home of the 10th U.S. Cavalry of Buffalo Soldiers so we have more Negros in town than most places in Montana. They keep to themselves mostly, but you will see them around sometimes."

Leo's employment by the Great Northern railroad gave him an in-depth understanding of its importance to the community. The train tracks paralleled the river and defined the northern edge of town. The railroad headquarters buildings were on the north side of Main Street and the center of the commercial district was on the south side.

As we walked along Main Street Leo pointed to some glass blocks in the sidewalk.

"Those provide light to one of the stranger parts of Havre. The Great Fire of 1904 destroyed most of the buildings at street level. The businesses moved to their basements so they could stay open while the stores were being rebuilt. They tunneled through and connected everything so you could walk from one shop to the next without coming up."

"That's interesting," I said. "Can we go see it?"

Leo looked at me with a smirk on his face. "Heavens, no. A lady of your caliber would never be seen down there now. It's home to many places of ill repute. Rumor has it there are opium dens and bordellos down there."

"Rumor only?" I said, while looking at Leo for a sign he might have been there. "You don't know it for a fact, do you?"

"Definitely not. Everyone in town would know and I'd be sent out of my home. It's mostly visited by the railroad men who come through here."

The prominence of the railroad caused the eastern edge of town to be the location of poorer housing and a string of bars frequented by many of the railroad men. However, the southern part of town was expanding and was home to many wealthy railroad and business families.

As we walked along the western end of First Street Leo pointed out the Montana Hotel and Grill. "The Montana opened a year ago," he said. "It has the finest rooms, and the best steaks in town. I go there often for dinner. And right next door is the Orpheum Theater."

"Oh – I love the theater," I exclaimed.

"Then you will be happy in Havre. In addition to the Orpheum, we have the Lyceum Theater right around the corner and an Opera House another block away. There are lots of entertainment opportunities here."

I could not restrain my excitement. "Oh, it is so wonderful. I can't wait to hear some good music and watch a good play. Do you like opera?"

Leo looked perplexed and said, "I've never been to an opera. It's not really my sort of music."

We continued down Third Street and Leo pointed out the Masonic Temple and the Elks Club. "Papa is already a member of the Elks, and has been a Mason for over twenty years," I mentioned. "I'm sure I will be going there."

Leo smiled. "I'm sure you will. The Elks has a dance every Friday night and the Masons are always sponsoring some sort of entertainment – a dinner dance, a masquerade, a community gathering."

"A dance every Friday," I exclaimed. "And I thought I was coming out to the wilderness. Havre has as much to offer as Grand Forks. Oh, it sounds like so much fun." I couldn't contain myself and was not being very ladylike. But I sensed Leo liked that about me.

"Would you like to go to the next dance at the Elks?" he asked.

Without hesitating I shrieked, "Yes – most definitely."

Leo and I became regulars at the Elks dances and many other venues in Havre.

Leo was a station clerk for the Great Northern. It was a good job with steady pay, but it also resulted in irregular hours. He spent most of his time at the Havre station, but since Havre was a hub and the railroad was expanding into more and more communities, he was frequently told to work at other stations for weeks at a time. Therefore, our times together were limited by his work schedule. We often went for days, or weeks, without seeing each other. But when we were together everything was wonderful.

Our personalities were similar in many ways. We wanted to be independent and enjoy new things. We didn't want to follow traditional ways. We could be warm and loving, but we were also both very argumentative and hotheaded. We argued over the silliest things, and then realized how stupid it was and made up. The making up was always wonderful.

Father and Mother liked Leo and approved of our dating. Father, in particular, thought Leo was a fine, upstanding young man with a strong, dominant personality and confidence. He had a good job, he was popular in town and knew all the important people. Both Father and Leo loved hunting and fishing. He became Father's favorite hunting partner. However, they both could be stubborn and egotistical. Sometimes they argued, but in the end, Father saw a man who could take care of his little girl, so the arguments always ended in peaceful accord.

Leo and I also had our differences. Leo was a westerner through and through. I had grown up in a Midwestern city and was innocent of the western ways. I enjoyed the theater, music, and art. He enjoyed being outdoors, riding, and hunting. I was an only child, and the few relatives I had were back in Minnesota. He was one of seven children in a family settled in Havre and the immediate area. I loved lace and ribbons. He loved getting dirty. He was Catholic while I was Episcopalian. Our biggest issue, though, was who was in charge. He wanted to be the dominating male. I wanted to be a strong, independent woman and make my own decisions. On that topic we never, ever, seemed to agree.

Father continued his busy building schedule. He was building all along the Great Northern route, better known as the Hi-Line. He also continued to build banks and commercial buildings in Havre, Chinook, and surrounding communities. When he wasn't on the job, he was hunting on the plains. The change of locale gave him new energy for his work, and he loved the wide-open spaces of Montana.

Mother's health had been a family issue for the last few years. In the summer of 1909, while we were still in Grand Forks, she traveled to Rochester, Minnesota, for a personal "female operation." Her recovery was slow and subject to frequent setbacks. For weeks at a time she would be fine and have her old strength and vigor back, but then she would have days of shortness of breath and dizziness. As a result of her ongoing health issues the local doctor thought it would be good for Mother to go to a milder climate in the winter. Mother's aunt and uncle lived in Seattle, Washington, and invited her to visit. Shortly after we got settled in Havre, in the fall of 1910, Mother went to Seattle. She returned refreshed and full of her old vigor. She could not stop talking about the trip, especially crossing the Rocky Mountains. "The mountains are so beautiful. The government recently opened Glacier National Park and it is beyond description. Mabel, this summer we are going to make a trip to Seattle – you will love it."

The plans for the trip were delayed when Grandmother Cynthia Richmond died in February 1911. Father, Mother and I boarded the eastbound express and returned to Melrose for the funeral. Grandmother Richmond had been one of the pioneers of Melrose, had lived in the area over fifty-five years, and was ninety-four years old. There was a large crowd at the funeral with much of Melrose attending. Afterward, we had a small family gathering with Father's sister, Harriet, her husband, Uncle George Miles, and my cousin Carlton, who came down from Fergus Falls. The return to Melrose was bittersweet though.

On the train back west I told Father and Mother, "Melrose wasn't the same as when we left. Most of my old friends have moved on and the town isn't what I remember from my childhood. It looked quaint, stale, and boring compared to the excitement and adventure I've found out west. I feel like a different person than when I left Melrose. Melrose was special, but my heart belongs to Montana."

"You've matured and experienced many things your friends in Melrose don't understand," said Mother. "You can't go back in life. You need to accept change and keep looking forward."

Father quietly nodded agreement. "Your Mother is right, Mabel. Life goes on and it isn't always the way you planned it. You must be ready for anything."

On our return to Havre we stopped in Grand Forks for a few days to visit old friends. We talked a school friend, Cassie Cummings, into coming west and going to Seattle with us. So, in March, 1911, Mother, Cassie, and myself boarded the Great Northern #1, the "Oriental Limited," to Seattle for a summer adventure. We visited family friends, explored the port city of Seattle, and went to the ocean. But the highlight of the trip was on the return. We stopped in Glacier National Park and spent a week at the Lake McDonald Lodge. I had never been to the mountains and this first experience was breathtaking. The snow-capped majesty of the mountains rising vertically from the deep blue mountain lakes amazed me. We hiked to the Continental Divide, rode the stage to the Many Glacier Hotel, and walked on glaciers. We saw all sorts of wildlife, but the bighorn sheep and mountain goats were the most spectacular. For a young lady from Minnesota it was the most wonderful and scenic place I had ever visited.

We returned to Havre and I started working part-time in Father's office. I loved living in Havre. I had plenty of friends, went out often, played cards until late, and slept in each morning. I didn't have a care in the world and had freedom to do as I wished. Havre had everything I needed. It was sophisticated, yet rustic. I could dress in the finest silks and lace for the Elks Club dances, or I could "go primitive," as we called it, wearing a plain cotton dress, with boots, my hair in braids and no hat for rides in the countryside. The city was big enough, but also small enough. I could walk downtown to shop, or go to the prairie all in the same day. And, of course, there was Leo. He made Havre a perfect place for me.

The men in line seemed to enjoy our story, but they were also curious. "So why are you in line for a homestead?" asked Elmer Slonaker. "It sounds like you are pretty well established in town."

Mother looked at Elmer and sighed. "Because E. C. Richmond is never satisfied."

Land!

"Belle, I've found the land I want." It was the fall of 1912.

Mother looked up from her morning tea and smiled at Father, "And what are you concocting now Edmond Richmond? I can tell this is another of your money-making schemes. Lately, they haven't been very successful."

Father was excited. "When I went hunting with Pete Peterson last month I found the perfect spot. It can be ours for next to nothing. I can build the big house you've always wanted Belle, and there are miles of open land for me to hunt. And I'll stop this construction stuff and traveling to different sites."

Mother was unimpressed. "And how much is this going to cost?"

"That's the thing," said Father, "next to nothing. I've been doing some research. Back in 1877 Congress passed the Desert Land Act to help settlement in dry lands throughout the west. It includes places like Arizona, New Mexico, Nevada, Colorado, Wyoming, the Dakotas, and – most importantly – Montana. It's similar to the Homestead Act but has two big differences. First, you can get 640 acres instead of the 320 the Homestead Act covers. Second, you don't have to live on the land, just irrigate it and cultivate it. In five years it's yours. I've got all the earth moving equipment already, so irrigation should be easy."

Mother still wasn't impressed. "Edmond, I've got everything I need right here in town. We've moved a lot in the last few years and I don't want to move again."

Father wasn't about to give up on this idea. "It only costs $1.25 per acre and we don't have to pay until we prove up in five years. I think you will love the scenery on the prairie and we can relax out there. But here's the other thing – if you don't like it, we can sell it for a profit. Montana is filling up fast with homesteaders and immigrants coming out to get the cheap, rich land. Word is the government is going to open up some of the land northeast of here for homesteading soon. I'm sure we would be able to sell it for good money. I don't think we can lose on the deal, Belle. Think about it."

The land was about thirty-five miles northeast of Havre and fifteen miles north of Chinook, in Blaine County. Blaine County was formed in 1912 from the eastern half of Hill County and Chinook, the small town twenty miles east of Havre, was named the county seat. When the area was opened to homesteading there would be a rush of settlers in the county. Father saw the opportunity to get involved in the growth early.

He continued talking without pausing, as if he knew our questions. "I'm almost sixty-one and it is time for me to slow down. Belle, your health hasn't been good. This will give me a chance to be home with you. Mabel can get a neighboring plot and have her own place. She has been anxious to get out on her own and settle down. Who knows, maybe Mr. Delorimier will be interested. I think it would be good for us all the way around."

Mother had stopped resisting Father's ideas. She had a tired, resigned look on her face, "It seems I cannot convince you to settle down Edmond. I'm very comfortable here in Havre, but I know you will continue to go after this land. If it doesn't cost anything more than a filing fee, I'll go along with it. I don't want to move, so you can take this land for your hunting."

I interjected, "I like living in the city, but I do love the prairie. I have music, dancing, cards, and Leo here for me. But I'm open to getting the land, if only for speculation."

The following week the three of us went to the Havre Land Office and filed claims for three 160 acre parcels of land under the Desert Land Act. Because the Act specified the claimant had to be the "Head of Household", Mother and I could not directly file the claim. Father paid Lloyd and Bruce Smith, two surveyors he knew, to apply for the land grants. Then they signed over the land to Mother and me. It was complicated, but all legal and quite common. Father also applied for a homestead on the remaining 160 acres. This was where he planned to build his dream house and settle down with Mother. All together we held all 640 acres of section two of township number thirty-five in Blaine County. This was the beginning of my life on the short-grass prairie of northern Montana.

Father had purchased a 1912 Ford Model T Touring car. He loved to brag it was the first automobile in Havre. One morning about a week after filing the claims we drove out to see our new land. It took all morning to drive cross-country, avoiding the coulees and deep ravines. We had a flat tire, but Father changed it quickly, telling us it was not unusual to get a flat driving across the prairie. We arrived shortly after noon to find a windswept piece of land with scrub brush, wild grasses, and not a tree in sight. I stood and turned around. I turned north, then east, then south, then west. It was all the same. Grass all the way to the horizon. I thought I knew the prairie, but this was wider and vaster than any place I had yet experienced. In one sense it was terrifying, but in another hypnotizing.

We walked the land and inspected the borders of our claim. When we came to the northern boundary Father stood and looked north.

"That's what we really want Mabel," he said. "That's the key piece of land for this whole area."

"What are you talking about Papa? I just see more grassland. Why is that so important?"

"There's a reservoir up there we can't see from here. I saw it while hunting, but the government survey was only finished a few months ago. It will be open to homesteading soon and we need to get claim to the land with the reservoir. Then we can control the water to this area and our property will be much more valuable. I have a plan, but I need your help."

Mother had been listening intently without saying anything. Now she spoke up. "Edmond, don't you dare get our daughter involved in one your speculation schemes. She's got enough responsibility already."

Father said, "Don't worry, Belle. I'm sure Mabel will like this plan. I have already filed for land under the Desert Land Act and also the Homestead Act. I want Mabel to file the claim for the land with the reservoir on it. She will be twenty-two and qualify as a head-of-household. She'll be able to apply for up to 320 acres if need be."

I was curious. "So the land would be in my name. It would be mine to live on?"

"Yes, that's the idea. Belle and I will live here and you will live on the land up north. We will only be about a half mile apart." Father was getting an excited gleam in his eyes again. "Mabel, you've been wanting a place of your own and this can be your chance to get started. Under the Homestead Act, you will have to live here, but we can work the land together. I'll still be doing construction jobs, but your mother and I can build here on this section, we will be close, and it will be a nice place for Belle to relax with you near. And, of course, we will increase the amount of land we own. That's a nice little benefit. We can keep all this and increase our holdings through homesteading. We will have the water and even more land to sell if we want. It's a gamble. We will have to file our claim early, before others do, but if we succeed it will work to our advantage."

"Sounds interesting. I could have a place of my own and you and Mother would only be a short walk away. Can I think about it?"

Father nodded. "Yep. For a couple more weeks. Then the land will be open for homesteading. The piece with the reservoir won't last long. Maybe you can talk to Mr. DeLorimer to see if he is interested too."

Father continued to think about it as he walked the fields. There was a small, dried creek bed near and Father immediately started calculating what he would have to do to use the creek for irrigation. Mother had been quiet for a long time, standing to the side and staring off toward the horizon. She asked me to walk with her. We found some fresh wildflowers and talked. She was unusually thoughtful.

"Mabel, you know your father will never stop dreaming of new places and new ideas. I'm finding it increasingly hard to keep up with him. I'm quickly fatigued and only want to rest and relax at home. But Edmond can never sit still for long. He has to keep moving. In spite of that, he has been a good husband and father and has given us freedom to find our own way. As a result, you have grown into an independent and strong young woman. Don't ever give up your stubborn, outspoken ways, and don't ever stop dreaming about the things you want to do. Be yourself and believe in yourself. Keep your optimism and hope. You may not see it right now, but this chunk of unforgiving land could be very beneficial to you in the future. Don't forget it or neglect it."

Father and I would drive out to the land on weekends. Mother resisted Father's land enthusiasm by staying in Havre. She was happy to stay home to knit and crochet. Father hauled earth-moving equipment to the land and cleared ravines and dug ditches for irrigation. He was always planning how he could improve the land, especially if we successfully claimed the irrigation pond. While he planned I would walk through the fields, pick wildflowers, and dream about living there someday. Sometimes Papa and I would hunt birds. On occasion Leo went with us. He and Papa would work or hunt, but he always found an excuse to walk with me. I would talk about living together and having a house on the prairie.

"Don't you think this would be a perfect spot for a house?" I'd say to him.

He would always hesitate, "I suppose. Yes, someday," was about all he would say.

"Why do you have to be so distant and noncommittal?" I'd ask. "You act like you don't want to be with me."

Leo looked at the horizon and said, "I want to be with you, but I'm not sold on being this far out of town. The railroad is moving me around a lot, and I've got a chance to be promoted. To live out here I'd have to leave my job. I don't know …" Then he usually would walk away and I'd be left standing alone with my uncertainty. I would be upset, but realized I couldn't change him. I vowed to make the most of our time together and try not to shape the future.

The Homestead Act was first passed by Congress in 1862. The Civil War was dividing the nation and the act was seen as a way to expand free, non-slave settlers into the lightly populated lands of the Great Plains. By limiting the amount of land to 160 acres, it enticed small, independent farmers and was not large enough to make use of slaves profitable. It became one of the most influential laws ever passed in America. After the war restless Americans and a mass of immigrants from Europe took advantage of the cheap land and wide open spaces, moving first into Nebraska and Iowa, then to the rest of the Great Plains. By the beginning of the twentieth-century settlers were looking to the high short grass prairies of the northern Plains.

The Dakotas filled with homesteaders in the 1880s and 1890s. Then Montana became the hotbed for homesteaders after the railroads went through, and especially after the passage of the Enlarged Homestead Act of 1909. The federal government slowly opened up land, starting in eastern Montana. As sections of land filled up they would open another section further west. By 1913 the settlement surge had reached Blaine and Hill counties and the land north of our desert claim became open for homesteading. It was what Father had been waiting for.

Homesteading

The Land Office door opened and the Department of Interior representative looked up and down the line. He finally looked back at the front of the line and acted like there must be some mistake.

"Good morning young lady. Are you holding a place for your husband?" It was March 12, 1913, and I had been sitting in line for three days. I was tired, but excited, and I found the office clerk's sarcasm annoying. I sensed a tone of disbelief and disrespect when he talked to me about the Homestead Act.

"No sir, I'm here to file my claim for a homestead," I said. I despised his attitude but was not going to let him get the best of me and foil my plans.

"Miss Richmond," he said as he looked over my filing form, "I'm sure a smart young lady like you knows the background of the Homestead Act, but I'm required to go over the requirements for filing a claim. You are probably aware President Lincoln signed the original Homestead Act into law back in 1862. The original law allowed settlers to get the patent to 160 acres of land if they lived on the land five years, improved it, and paid a five-dollar filing fee. The rules are now basically the same, but the Enlarged Homestead Act of 1909 has expanded your opportunities. You can now claim up to 320 acres of land. The railroad people, who wanted new settlers up here on the Hi-Line, pushed the law through Congress. You still have to build a residence and improve the land, and you must live on the land at least seven months out of the year. If you can do those things and have two witnesses swear you have met all the requirements – what we call 'proving up your claim' – you can apply for the patent to the land in three years instead of the original five years. The price has also increased to twenty-five dollars. Any questions?"

"None at all," I said confidently. "I've done my home-work and read all the rules."

He continued in a rather condescending tone, "You are single I see. Do you understand married women are not permitted to homestead since they aren't the legal head of the household? Also, if you marry prior to proving up your claim it can become complicated. Your husband will then have to meet the requirements and prove up in his name, which may take longer. Do you understand?"

I nodded. "Yes, I am aware of all that."

"And do you know where you want to settle?"

"Yes sir. I know exactly. I wish to stake a claim to 320 acres in the southeast quarter of section twenty-six, and the eastern half of the east half, of section thirty-five. It is in township thirty-six north of range twenty east of the Montana Meridian." I had been memorizing the legal description of the spot for a week with Father's help.

"Whoa - very impressive." The clerk said as he wrote it all down. "Most come in here with only a vague idea of what they want and have no idea of the legal description of the land. Where did you learn that?"

"My family – my father, mother, and I – have already claimed acreage adjacent to that plot through the Desert Land Act. We filed last year. But this new land is going to be my place. I'm going to be living there, so I wanted to know everything about it. I wanted to know exactly where it was."

The clerk looked at the Blaine County map and then looked up at me. " I suppose you know your claim includes a dam and the Soo Reservoir?"

"Oh yes. It is the main reason we want to be there. My father and I have already been to the land and scouted it out."

"Sounds like your father is quite involved in all this," he said. "I'd say you're pretty lucky to have someone to help you out. Have you and your father discussed the problems having water on your land can cause?"

"What type of problems?" I felt he was trying to see if I scared easily, so I made sure I kept my confidence.

He looked at me with a very serious look in his eye. "Having a reliable source of water out here on the high plains can bring you unwanted friends and even 'water rustlers'."

I thought about the implications of what he was saying. Stories had been going around for years of ranchers and farmers diverting water from another's land - what they called "water rustling". It had led to many fights, court cases, and even some shootings. But I couldn't worry about it right now, and I wasn't going to back down, so I confidently said, "I'll deal with that when, and if, I have to. This is the plot of land I want." I laid out the twenty-five dollars for the filing fee, sat back, and looked at the clerk.

He filled out the rest of the paperwork and said, "Sign here and it will be yours. Best of luck Miss Richmond."

And that was it. The land Father and I had been looking at for over a year was mine. All I had to do now was the work –

and hard work didn't scare me. I was excited and apprehensive at the same time. I had succeeded, with Papa's help, in obtaining a piece of land to call my own. It would finally be a chance for me to be independent. Success or failure would depend on me. I intended it to be a success.

I was now part of an exciting period in Montana history. Thousands of homesteaders had come to Montana in the four years since the Enlarged Homestead Act of 1909 had been passed, and even more were coming after me. In the next few years Montana's population would double due to the influx of new settlers, all attracted to the rich, and virtually free, land available.

The railroads, especially James J. Hill's Great Northern Railroad, had done everything possible to encourage settlement along what was known as the Hi-Line – the route the Great Northern took across the northern stretch of states from Minneapolis to Seattle. They placed ads and posters throughout the Eastern and Midwestern states making promises about the rich land. They also sent information and agents to Europe to attract immigrants to settle in North Dakota and Montana. These ads emphasized cheap land, fertile soil, and showed huge fields of grain. Montana was described as the land of milk and honey. One pamphlet, when describing Montana, claimed "it is questionable if any state in the union has a better climate" and winters were "less severe than in areas farther east." The Great Northern provided transportation from St. Paul to the west for as little as ten dollars a family, and you could fill up a boxcar with personal supplies and building materials for less than twenty-five dollars. With all these opportunities to own land and get rich farming, it was no wonder thousands and thousands moved to Montana.

New methods of "scientific farming" were being developed and promoted by the railroads to encourage settlement of the plains. The leading example of scientific farming was "dry-land farming" promoted by H. W. Campbell in his *Soil Culture Manual*. The idea was the soil would maintain a natural amount of moisture if properly cared for. The fields needed to be plowed deep to break up the grasses. The deep plowing was intended to allow what moisture there was to soak deep enough to help the roots of the crop. The seeds were planted in the late summer or early autumn to take advantage of the autumn rains and winter snows. Then they would be ready for harvesting in the early summer. Each season would require alternating fields to allow the old one to go fallow and restore the natural nutrients. The system worked in the eastern Dakotas. The most famous statement of Mr. Campbell's was the "rain will follow the crops." It made sense and seemed to be an easy method of farming. It was my plan to practice "dry-land farming" on my homestead.

I filed my claim in early March, but rough spring weather and Father's jobs prevented us from getting out to the land before the middle of April. Even in Papa's Model T it took almost four hours to cover the thirty-five miles to the claim, but when we finally arrived it was beautiful. The sun was high in the dark blue sky, with a few puffy white clouds. The earth was covered with native grasses stretching to the horizon in every direction. There was not a tree in sight. To the south was the outline of the Bear Paw Mountains. Turning west, I saw the Sweet Grass Hills on the distant horizon. To the north was a long line of rolling hills known as Cherry Ridge. The Canadian border was only ten miles away.

We walked the land. It was rich and had never been broken by a plow. The knee-high prairie grass waved in a gentle breeze. We crested a gentle rise and looked around. In front of us was a slight depression protected by the higher land. The reservoir was only a hundred yards away. "This will be a perfect spot for your house," said Father. "You are close to the pond, but far enough away you won't have to worry about flooding. The surrounding land is high enough to give you a view, but still protect you from the weather, especially from the north, where that little rise and the pond will offer a break to the wind. Over there to the west is a good field for crops. I think it looks good."

The pond was created by an earthen dam on a small, seasonal creek – locally called a coulee. The Army Corps of Engineers built the dam a few years earlier, but Father had repaired it and improved it after claiming the land to the south. The pond covered almost forty acres and would be a valuable asset to any farm in the area. It was all mine if I could fulfill the homestead requirements. I was confident I could.

Leo claimed the 160 acres to the east of my claim. Our plan was to accumulate as much land as possible. When we got married – something I was convinced was going to happen soon – we would own 480 acres to farm and ranch. My dream was coming to fruition. I would have a place of my own, and my parents would build on the land to the south and be a half mile away. Leo would be right next door and, hopefully, we would soon be living together as husband and wife. It was all too perfect.

Death of My Soul

My world changed on May 30, 1913.

"Papa, come quick," I screamed. "Mama isn't moving. I think she's dead. Oh God! Come quickly Papa. Please don't die Mama."

Father rushed into the kitchen and looked at his wife sitting in a chair, a teacup still in her hand, with her head slumped over. He reached for her but realized it was too late.

With a quiet look of resignation, he asked, "What happened?"

"I'm not sure," I sobbed. "I got Mother her morning tea, like I do every day, then walked out of the room for a minute. When I came back she was slumped over. Oh my God. Is she dead Papa?" I was crying uncontrollably.

Father looked serious. He sternly and stoically told me, "Get ahold of yourself, Mabel, and call Dr. Bassow's office. We need him immediately."

The doctor came quickly, but by then there was no question. Mother was dead. She was only fifty-six years old. Too young for a heart attack, but that was what the doctor said it was. "Probably due to chronic valvular [sic] heart-disease" was the cause listed on her death certificate. Although Father believed it was a result of the rheumatic fever eight years earlier, I was certain the true cause was a broken heart. Mother had not been the same since leaving Melrose. She stayed loyal to her husband and went with him on his journeys, but her heart was always in Minnesota. She hated leaving her home and family, and although she professed to like Montana and Havre, her spirit had never been quite the same.

Everything changed with her death. She had been not only my mother and mentor, but also my best friend. We were traveling companions. She taught me to love music and the theater. She taught me the complicated expectations of a turn-of-the-century woman and what it meant to be a lady. And she talked to me. For as long as I could remember she had talked to me as an adult – not as her child. We discussed everything – politics, community events, men. We often spoke in private because those topics weren't polite for a lady to express in public. I knew immediately my life would never be the same.

Mother's death changed Father, too. He became more introverted. He no longer had his wife as a buffer between us. She had been his anchor and the person who kept him on task. She provided order to his hectic life, watched the finances, and kept him from dreaming too much. He was the worker and wage earner, but she was the more intelligent half of the partnership. Without her guidance Father no longer had a voice of reason to monitor his speculative gambles and spontaneous decisions. He would not listen to me as he had listened to her. He became more demanding, more distant, and more eccentric. His moods were more unpredictable. I knew he still loved me, but he could not express it anymore. Although Father was still very much alive, a large part of him died on Memorial Day 1913.

Mary Isabell Conner Richmond was returned to her beloved Melrose for burial. It took three excruciating days to travel back. Three days where I sat next to her casket in shock and disbelief. I cried until I could cry no more. A large group of friends and mourners met us at the Melrose station. Her body was taken directly to the Episcopal Church for the funeral and then to Oak Hill Cemetery for burial. The cemetery was located east of town on a lovely oak-shaded hillside set back from the road to St. Cloud. She was buried in the Richmond plot, next to Grandfather Reuben, Grandmother Cynthia, and my sister, Hattie Belle. Her parents – the Conners – were buried nearby. Both families had been founding members of the Melrose community.

In its obituary, the *Melrose Beacon* summarized her life saying, "She was widely known and numbered her friends by her acquaintants [sic]. None ever entered her home without a warm welcome. None left without feeling the warmth of genuine hospitality ... the memory of her will ever be green in the minds and hearts of her many friends."

We stayed in Melrose for a week. We realized we would not be returning to Melrose to live so Father sold the house we had been renting out. Father was uncomfortable the entire time in town. There were too many memories of the old days – the days of fun and frolic with Belle. I think he realized how much had changed since he took us away from Melrose. I know I did.

While in Melrose, our old preacher met with us and gave us ways to deal with our grief. He suggested I start keeping a journal to write down my feelings and compartmentalize my pain. I had always enjoyed writing verses and poetry, so this seemed like something I could do to lessen my grief. I started keeping a diary. It never replaced Mother for companionship, but it gave me solace and a chance to reflect on my life like I had never done before.

On the train back to Montana Father presented me with Mother's old scrapbook.

"I found this while going through Belle's things," he said reverently. "She was so proud of our families and what we have done. I know she would want you to have it. You have to carry on the legacy of the Richmonds and the Conners."

Tears came to my eyes as I took the book and held it close to my heart. "I will do my best to make Mama and you proud," I said. "I will treasure this for the rest of my life." I have it still.

As I read and reread the clippings and writings in the scrapbook I remembered many of Mother's favorite sayings and wrote them in my new diary.

"Family first. That's always most important."

"Look to the future and grasp the opportunities in front of you."

"Change is hard, but necessary. Make change a positive event."

"Life is like a good book. It is a series of chapters, all leading to the grand conclusion. You may briefly look back, but you've already been there so you want to look ahead. Turn the page."

Her last advice to me seemed even more prophetic at this time. "Don't ever give up your stubborn, independent streak, and don't stop dreaming about the people and places you love. Keep your optimism and hope."

My life was changed forever. Mother's death made me realize I could no longer be "momma's little girl." I had to stand on my own and be myself. I knew Father would only be indirectly involved – he would continue to travel, hunt, and have his unpredictable moods. I had to grow up and become the woman my mother would approve of. My days of lace dresses, fancy hairstyles, makeup, and ladylike politeness were over. They might return someday, but in the meantime I had to be strong, independent, and self-reliant. It was time for me to move on with my life.

The High Plains

June and July of 1913 were a blur. Father and I returned to Havre seriously depressed. Neither of us wanted to talk about Mother's death, but everywhere we went people offered their condolences and thoughts, which only aggravated our grieving. Father tried to ignore the loss by working late and taking on extra tasks. I tried to return to the social scene of Havre, playing cards, going to theater and opera, and associating with old friends. Neither method kept us from our grief of losing Mother. We talked about the homestead and the land often, but made no attempts to do anything there.

"Papa," I said, "I don't think I can go ahead with the plans for the homestead without Mother's support. I'm not sure I can go do it."

Father had the opposite opinion. "Mabel, the best thing for us would be to go out to the prairie and get ourselves wrapped up in the work out there. Your mother wasn't crazy about the homesteading idea for herself, but she always said it would be a good opportunity for you. We really must go."

For the first time in a long time, I didn't have any confidence and was unsure of what to do. "I feel lost. I don't think I can do it. I don't think I can live out there without her."

"I'll be there, and so will Leo, I'm sure. I'm more depressed here in town. I've got to get out to the open spaces. Next week we will go to the homestead."

It was the middle of August before we finally drove to the homestead. We determined to stay on the land and work out our frustrations and disappointment. Neither of us talked about Mother. We followed Mother's advice, "You've got to move on. Don't look back."

Establishing my home on the prairie became our therapy. We refused to return to Havre until I was settled on the homestead. We slept under the stars, ate over a campfire, and worked on the ranch. Neither of us had ever broken ground or done any extensive farming, but we were determined to learn, even if it was through trial and error. There were plenty of errors, but we learned.

I was lazy, naïve, and unenthused about doing the fieldwork. I preferred walking through the grasses and wildflowers. Father became focused on building me a nice house, so he didn't do much to get me going. He would say things like, "I think you should start plowing today," but then did nothing to help harness the horses or motivate me to get the work done. We didn't realize how much time was necessary to break the soil and prepare the land for planting.

A typical homestead shack might only be an eight-by-ten-foot shelter with tarpaper siding. Father felt such a simple building was beneath his expertise and would ruin his reputation. He wanted to build me the best house possible, which required more lumber than most. Consequently, he had to make numerous trips to Chinook to get lumber and haul it out to the land. It took him almost two weeks to get the materials. He brought some of his workers out to help and within a matter of days, my place was done. It was lovely. It wasn't huge, but compared to most homestead shacks it was luxurious. It was only twelve feet by sixteen feet, but it had a glass window on each side, a stove for cooking and heating, a table, and a foldaway bed. I made curtains for the windows and found some lace to put on the table. It soon looked like home. I still referred to it as "my shack," but it was much more comfortable than most places on the prairie.

After building the house, Father went to work building a barn. Within a week he had a thirty-by-thirty-foot barn big enough for our team of horses and storage of his earth-moving equipment.

I slowly learned how to work the land. We had four horses and a new plow, but the virgin soil was almost impossible to break. The roots of the prairie grasses were over two feet deep and had never been touched. The soil was heavy and baked to a concrete consistency. My first pass with the plow was worthless, as it barely scratched the surface. The horses were big and strong and it took all my strength to keep them on a line. It took three different passes and ten days of work to turn over a mere ten acres of land. I was exhausted and afraid I would never be able to set a furrow deep enough to get a good crop in.

On September seventh the house was completed and Father and I spent our first official night of residency on the homestead. The Homestead Act required a physical presence on the land for seven months of the year and cultivation of one-sixteenth of the land – which would be twenty acres. By the end of September we knew there was no way to meet those requirements before we submitted our paperwork for the first year's proof. It seemed so futile we decided to let the ten acres I had turned over to lay fallow until next spring and not plant any seed.

Father was around more than he had ever been in the past and was surprisingly supportive. He wanted to see me succeed on the ranch and provided encouragement to me whenever he could. He would say things like, "This isn't so bad, Mabel. This place is becoming quite comfortable. I'm sure you will love it out here. I'll be here most of the time to keep you company." And most of all, he would point out something like, "Leo is right next door and all the other neighbors seem very nice. They will keep you company."

His encouragement and the hard work helped me improve my attitude and restored my hope for the future. The longer I was on the prairie the more I appreciated the strange magnetism of the land. I realized this was not going to be a good year, but I didn't need to worry about it. I would be living in town for the winter and next year I would get my crops planted early, live on the farm, and get a good year under my belt. I began to believe in what I was doing.

Leo was very sympathetic and supportive. He had been with me a lot when I was in town and now came over whenever he was at his homestead. He built a small shack on his land. It was not as large, or complete as mine, but he said it was fine for him. He had been very compassionate since I returned from Mother's funeral. He was even more important to me since I had lost my closest confidante. He would spend hours listening to my dreams and thoughts about the homestead and the future. He never really said much, but it helped when he listened. I was sure he agreed with my plans for the future.

He plowed enough acreage to meet the requirement for improving the land, but he didn't seem too concerned about putting in a crop. Like me, he realized it was too late in the year and was preparing the land for next spring. While I was becoming excited about the farm and impatient to get things done, he seemed to approach it with dread and apprehension. Finally, one day in mid-October, I questioned him.

"Don't you love it out here? Aren't you excited about getting a crop in and improving this place?"

He looked away from me and quietly said, "I suppose so – but not as much as you are."

"I've noticed you sometimes seem to be dreading the work."

He turned back to me and said with a pained look, "I don't want to disappoint you Mabel, but I can't get excited about this place. Maybe I'm just not set out to be a farmer. I've always wanted land out here and think this is a great opportunity, but I still have my job with the railroad. They are making more and more demands on me. I've been offered a new job as a station manager, which will mean I have to be in Havre more. It's a good job and pays well. To me, this land is more like a hobby or something to keep for hunting."

The implications of what he was saying hit deep. He had been going back and forth to Havre often. He would be in town for a week, and then come out to the land for three or four days until his next shift on the railroad. But this new job meant he would have regular hours every week and his times on the homestead would be few and far between.

I thought about it and remembered what Mother said about worrying about the future. "We'll have to make it work. I will stay here in the summer and come to town when I can. I am coming back to Havre in the winter, and we will have much more time together then. We can do it."

Leo looked over and smiled, "Thank you for understanding. As you say, we will have to make it work."

As winter approached I watched, studied, and learned to read the weather of the plains. The days grew shorter and the nights colder. The grasses dried and changed colors. The weather was unpredictable and often violent. Rains were infrequent, but when they came they could be hard and real gully-washers. The wind was nonstop, usually cold and stinging out of the north, but when a south wind came across the dry, open plains you thought it was July again. Two days later it could snow.

As the days shortened, I realized the land required more work than I could handle myself. Even when Father and Leo were around we couldn't finish everything. Father contacted a hired hand to help, but I was uncomfortable being by myself with him, so he only came when Father was there – which wasn't nearly enough. Papa was frequently gone. Usually he would say it was for work, but sometimes I think he just wanted to get away. I didn't always know where he was, and if I asked, he wouldn't tell. I needed to take advantage of his help when he was there and do the best I could when he wasn't.

Leo also wasn't there as much as I wanted. It was a short walk from his land to mine, but I usually only saw him once or twice a week. The Great Northern was still his main job, so he was usually in Havre. He would come to the ranch on weekends, but he had to work his own land. Our times together were wonderful, but the separations were terrible. We continued to have our ups and downs. There were times when we couldn't talk to each other, but then there were times I treasured. In my diary I wrote, "Leo came [over] and the least said the better...we had a very unhappy evening. Oh, why do we have to be so horrid once in a while?" But three days later I wrote, "Leo came up in the afternoon and oh, it has been so happy that I should write this with red ink." Every day was a different emotion.

By early November I was ready to move back to Havre for the winter. I had plowed and harrowed the fields and they were ready for spring planting, but in the meantime there was nothing else to do. My house was not winter-proof, and Father and I still had our house in town. I needed time in town to evaluate my situation on the homestead, relax, help Father in his business, and prepare for next year. We closed things up, took our horses to the livery, and moved back to town.

Leo and Me

Life in town was a total contrast to life on the homestead. In Havre, I lived in the comfort of my father's house, worked part-time at his office, and made my own schedule. I stayed out late playing bridge and entertaining friends then slept late in the morning. Best of all, I could see Leo much more often. We had meals together. We were bridge partners. We went to dances at the Elks, shows at the Orpheum, and even opera. But there were still obstacles we couldn't seem to overcome – mainly religion, who was in charge, and where to live.

Our relationship was fine before the Christmas holiday. We had not had a serious disagreement in weeks. A few days before Christmas Leo asked me to his house for dinner. I had met his family before, of course, but had not spent much time with them. They were always very friendly and I thought we got on well. Therefore I was surprised when Leo said, "Remember, do not bring up religion around my parents. They don't know you aren't Catholic."

I looked at him in exasperation, "What! Haven't you told them? We've been dating for almost three years and my religion has never been an issue before."

"I've never said anything to them because they've never asked," he said reluctantly.

"Are our religious differences a problem for you?" I asked.

"Not really. I'm not deeply into the Church, but my parents are, and I think it would really upset my mother. She is a very traditional French Canadian Catholic. So let's not bring it up and do our best to enjoy Christmas."

"Well – when do you plan to tell her? Aren't we going to get married?" We had discussed marriage before and I knew Leo hated the topic, but it had to be said. "Are you just trying to hide it? You know that isn't going to work. Or don't you want to marry me? Is that why you don't want to talk about it?" I was getting more frustrated and angry the more I talked about it.

"Look, my parents are expecting us. Can't we have dinner with my family without arguing about religion or marriage?" Leo was doing his best to control his temper and deflect the conversation. "Let's smile and pretend everything is great. You and I can discuss this later."

I was not going to let it go easily. "Why wait? Nothing's going to change. You don't want to discuss it because you don't want to marry me. I'm just a nice companion for you – right? Would you rather upset me than your mother? Suddenly I don't think I want to go to this family dinner. I don't know what I should say or not say. What will we talk about?" I was angry and Leo knew it.

"Settle down Mabel," he said, trying to stay calm himself. "We will talk this over, and no, it's not a question of marrying you. I love you, but it isn't the time to discuss marriage. We have too many things to work out – where we would live, jobs, and the homesteads. And that doesn't even include the religion thing. Can't you go to this dinner and smile and be friendly to my family? I know you can do it. I've seen you do it before. Okay?"

"Whatever you want, but I'm not happy about all this."

The dinner went fine and Leo's family was very nice, but as we were getting ready to leave Leo's mother innocently asked, "Will you be going to Christmas Eve Mass with us, Mabel?"

I didn't know what to answer and hesitated too long. "Umm, I don't know, Leo and I haven't talked about it." But Leo's mother knew something was wrong.

"You are Catholic aren't you?" she asked.

Leo stepped in quickly. "We'll talk about Mass later, Mother. I haven't said anything about it to Mabel."

I don't think his mother believed him, but she let the subject die. As Leo walked me home we both knew it was not going to be an easy subject to discuss. Finally he said, "Just let it rest for a while. I'll give Mother an excuse for you not going to Mass with us. In the meantime, I'll work on her a little. Maybe in another month or two she will see it doesn't matter."

"Something tells me that's not going to be the case, but if you want to let it simmer, fine. Sooner or later we will have to tell your family I'm not Catholic."

"I prefer it is later," Leo said.

On New Year's Eve Leo and I joined most of Havre at the Elks dance to welcome in 1914. Little did I know how significant 1914 would be to the world, the nation, and me. By the end of the year most of the world, except the United States, would be at war, women would gain the right to vote in Montana, and I would live the first full year of my life without

Mama as my friend and guide. I was determined to remember her teachings and become the woman she raised me to be.

After the New Year's dance, we went to the Delorimiers' house and played cards until 3:00 a.m. I stayed there, slept on the couch, and the next day went to an afternoon meal at the new house of some friends.

January and February marked the social season in Havre, and Leo and I were regular participants in the activities. During the week I would help at Father's office, sew, cook, and keep house. But the weekends consisted of dinner parties, cards, movies, theater, and dances, frequently lasting until two or three in the morning. Leo and I were always invited and had great fun.

Father, on the other hand, grew more and more distant. He would hunt and fish by himself or go to the Masons and Elks to drink. His moods were unpredictable, and whenever I tried to talk about it, he would storm out of the house and disappear for hours. He would never talk about Mother. I became increasingly worried about him.

The weather was especially unpredictable. In early January we experienced a Chinook wind – a warm breeze that came down the mountains and melted the snow. It made us all think spring was coming early. But as soon as we were getting used to the warmth, the temperatures plunged. On February third a temperature of minus thirty was recorded at the Havre train station. The next day temperatures continued to drop to a record of minus forty-six degrees. The night was miserable. My lights went out, the pipes froze, water flooded the kitchen, and the fires went out in my stoves. I went over to my neighbors, the MacCartheys, for the night. The next day the plumber was at the house all day fixing the pipes. After he left I had to clean up the mess myself, since Father was again out of town.

Although it was miserable in town, I was especially concerned about Leo. He had gone to his homestead the week before to check on a report his cabin had been broken into. He told me later nothing was taken or damaged. He figured it was a drifter looking for a place to get out of the weather for a few days. But the terrible winter weather forced him to stay out on the prairie for over two weeks.

I wanted him to return to Havre but knew the weather was too bad for traveling. I wrote him two long letters describing how much I missed him and how I wanted him home. I'm not sure they ever made it to his shack, but it felt good to write down my feelings.

The frigid cold did not let up until early March. When the weather finally broke Leo returned to town, but for some reason didn't tell me. Since it was warmer I decided to walk into town. I still thought Leo was stuck on the prairie. As I turned onto Main Street, I saw him walking toward the railroad offices. When I caught up to him he tried to give me a hug, but I resisted.

"What are you doing here? Why didn't you tell me you were back in town? When did you get back?" I was full of questions, but also anxiety because he was being so secretive.

Leo looked perplexed, "I got back late last night. I was dirty and tired and didn't want to bother you, so I went home."

"You didn't want to bother me? I've been worried sick about you for two weeks and missed you terribly. You never wrote. I was afraid you had frozen out there. Didn't you miss me? Didn't you want to see me?"

Leo looked confused and didn't know what to say, "I'm sorry. I desperately wanted to get home."

"You wanted to get home? Home apparently doesn't include me." Leo was looking around nervously at people walking by us on the street. "I see you don't want to talk to me right now, so I'll go. Good-bye." I was hurt, angry, and confused. I didn't know what Leo wanted with our relationship. I went home and tried to sort things out.

In the evening Leo came over and apologized. "I'm sorry. I had a terrible time at the homestead. All I wanted was to get home. I should have come over last night, but I wanted to get home and sleep in my own bed."

By then I had calmed down. I couldn't stay mad at him for long – he was too special to me. "Do you still want to be with me? Earlier today you were treating me like a stranger on the street. Do you still love me?"

Leo smiled, "Of course I still love you. I didn't know what to do today in town. I wanted to kiss you, but I also know you don't like show affection in public."

"Mother taught me it's not ladylike to kiss and hug in the middle of the street. But we're not in the street now..."

Leo took the hint and leaned over and gave me a big hug and kiss. Making up with him was wonderful. Leo stayed with me, but we did not sleep together. We both agreed premarital sex was unacceptable.

The next morning we took a long walk through town, window-shopping, laughing, and talking. Everything was good.

Except for Father. He became more depressed. He said it was "cabin fever" and complained of being cooped up by the bad weather, but I believed he was missing Mother. He wouldn't admit it, but I could tell she was always on his mind. He would be gone until late at night, usually at the Masonic Temple, the Elks Club, or a bar downtown. I knew he was drinking and was concerned about him. He was still working, although the jobs came in much slower and were not as profitable as they once had been. He was still in good health, but his attitude and solitude became an issue.

It was an eventful spring for all of us. Papa turned sixty-two on March fourth, and Mother would have been fifty-seven on March twenty-first. Emotions were strong and we were on edge for each birthday. Mother's, in particular, brought tears and memories for Father and me. We tried to conduct business as usual, but it didn't work. Leo came over and tried to distract me, while Father packed for a business trip to North Dakota. Father and I went to the Havre Land Office and made our yearly proof and applied for the final paperwork on the land claimed with the Desert Land Act. But none of this helped take our minds off Mother's death. We were both quiet and irritable throughout the day.

A few days later, while Father was on his business trip, Leo came to our house for dinner. After dinner we sat on the couch and talked.

"I'm moving back to the homestead next week," Leo said. "What does your father think about us being together?"

"Papa likes you a lot, Leo," I said. "We've been together for a long time. He enjoys having you around and appreciates your help out at the homestead. You like to hunt and fish with him. I don't see a problem. Why do you ask?"

"Oh, I know he likes hunting and fishing with me. But sometimes he gets angry and I'm not sure what he wants from me. I don't know if he wants me as a son-in-law."

I was a bit surprised by the questioning, "I'm sure he likes you. He's told me so. You must remember it's been a very stressful year for him. Mother's death and a slowdown in business have really affected him. He is more isolated and depressed this past year than previously and he's drinking more."

"What about you? Are you happy with me?"

"Leo – I love you. You know that."

He leaned over and kissed me, and then we kissed some more. It was so good and I was lost in the moment. I didn't want it to end. The next thing I knew we were in bed together, having forgotten our earlier promise about premarital sex. Oh, it was wonderful.

The next morning, after Leo left for work, I wrote in my diary, "What a wonderful day. Why can't every day be so sweetly joyously brim full of happiness? I mean to make them so if I have anything to do about it."

Alone on the Prairie

In April I bought a house in Havre, even though I was anxious to get back to the homestead. Father had moved into the apartment above his office on Fourth Street and it was too small for both of us. It was time for a place of my own in the winter. I still had hesitations about living on the prairie and had not completely given up on the idea of living in town. I thought I could spend the summers at the homestead and winter in town. Besides, this gave me an option if life on the prairie did not work out. It was a small bungalow in a new part of town, on the corner of Fifth Avenue and Seventh Street, but it was all I needed. Actually Father paid for the house, but I was listed as the owner. I think he was glad I had my own place.

Leo and I had another discussion about our future and he was adamant he did not want to live full time on the prairie. I felt if I owned a house in Havre it might help our relationship and convince him I could live in the city part of the year. It was fun decorating and making it feel like home, but I eventually realized I wouldn't be spending much time there.

Soon after buying the house Father and I returned to the homestead. I was pleased with how it had survived the winter without any damage. There weren't even any mice in the shack and within no time we had everything cleaned up and I was cooking lunch. It felt good to get back to my little place.

Father only stayed two days then surprised me by saying he had to go back to Havre.

"Mabel, before I go I have to tell you something I've been thinking about all winter. I can't live out here. I'm going to stay in Havre."

I was shocked. It had always been his idea – his dream – to get this land and start a new life.

He saw my surprise and said, "I can't live here without Belle. I cannot do it without her. I'm going to stay in Havre and continue my building. I have been awarded the contract to build the public library in Havre – you know, the one Mr. Andrew Carnegie is paying for. The job will keep me busy for most of the next year. And I still have my connections with the Great Northern and can get plenty of jobs with them. It may mean I'll be gone more, but you have Leo now and are strong enough to get along on your own."

"But Papa, I thought you wanted to share the homesteading with me. You were going to build right over there," as I pointed south to a small ridgeline.

"I can't do it. It was always a speculative piece of land anyway. I'm not a farmer and I know I never will be. My plan was to build a place out here for Belle and me to relax in. I was just going to be a gentleman farmer. I know the Homestead Act says I have to improve the land and live on it, but I can't do it right now. Maybe I'll build something later. Right now I have too many memories of your mother. I can't live here without her. I need to keep working so I don't think of her constantly. And I need the money. I've spent a lot lately and don't have much in the bank. It just has to be."

"But what am I going to do? All you do is think about yourself. You expect me to stay out here alone?" I was panicking, thinking of being totally on my own.

"Yes – you have to or we will lose the land." Father always thought of possessions first. "You can do it. I will come out and help you whenever I can. I'll come on weekends and whenever you need me. We will get a crop in and all you will have to do is watch it grow. I'll hire a farmhand to help you."

"It's not so simple. If you knew anything about farming you would understand," I shrieked.

But he insisted and there was no way to change his mind. Within the hour he was motoring back to Havre.

Suddenly I was alone. When Father left I sat on the stoop and cried. The emotional stress and fears of being alone came crashing down on me. I knew Father would not be back for weeks or months at a time, and Leo was in Havre. I looked around. I was totally isolated out in the middle of the prairie with no one to talk to or confide in. I had always had friends and family for company. I didn't know how I would handle the loneliness.

I remembered the Melrose preacher who recommended I write in a journal to express my concerns and fears. I had not been consistent in my diary entries, but I realized this was a perfect time to become more loyal to my diary and I vowed to be more vigilant with my writing. It would give me an escape from the isolation. In the evening I wrote of my loneliness. "Oh, it's so beastly lonely … I'm so far from anyone."

I was depressed, but as I lay in bed listening to the coyotes howl and the wind sweep across the plains, I made a decision. I was going to make this work. I was strong and smart and could make this homestead mine. I had neighbors I hadn't met. I had work to do. That's what Mother would want me to do. Face the future and accept it. Quit looking for help from others and help myself. I could do it.

As a symbol of my new life I made a dramatic decision. I would cut my hair. I had never had more than a trim. It reached down to my waist and had been a point of pride as I was growing up. Mother had always fussed over my hair and said how beautiful it was. I had always worn it up or in a long braid. But if I was going to live alone on the prairie my hair needed to be much easier to care for. I was going to get dirty and sweaty doing farm work and long hair wasn't practical. I took out my scissors and cut it to shoulder length. I did it quickly so I wouldn't change my mind, then just as quickly started crying when I saw it all lying on the floor. But I was determined to start a new life and this was the first step.

The next morning I climbed on my horse and set out to do something I should have done much earlier – meet my neighbors. I discovered a wonderful group of people who were glad to meet me. To the west, within earshot of my shack, were Elmer and Bessie Slonaker. Elmer was the gentleman in line with me at the Land Office and had claimed the land on the other side of our reservoir, but had not moved out right away. Bessie had been pregnant with their second child, so they waited until little Donald was born before moving to their homestead. I particularly liked Bessie. She was my age, out-going, energetic, and a joy to be around. She was smart, strong, and very personable. We became the best of friends.

To the south I met Alma Tinker, another single woman trying to make it on her own. Next to Alma were two married couples, the Furchtbars and the Ovesens. My neighbors became my constant companions, card partners, and helpful in many ways. Farther south, but less than a mile away were the Robertsons, the Crofts, and the Petersons, couples who were always willing to help a neighbor. I returned home with a new attitude and a burst of energy. I'd met wonderful people who shared my outlook and perspective on life. We were all optimistic about our future on the prairie. We were a small community with like interests.

Our mailing address was Cherry Ridge, Montana, even though it was almost ten miles away and consisted of only four buildings, counting the post office. I soon discovered distances meant nothing on the prairie. Having neighbors a half mile or a mile away meant they were close. When someone went to the post office or store they would pick up mail or supplies for all of us, then spend the rest of the day delivering what they picked up and discussing any news they learned. There was a closeness unheard of in the city. My neighbors and I helped each other get our farms started. We laughed, sweated, and dreamed together. We did our wash, cooked, and ate together. We talked politics, religion, education, children, and, of course, ranching. We became closer than anyone could imagine.

The nearest community of any size was Chinook, which was about thirteen miles away across the prairie. Chinook had been named county seat of Blaine County when the county was formed in 1912 and was growing steadily, with a population of almost 800 souls. It had a small hotel, The First State Bank, O'Hanlon's Mercantile, Lehfeldt's Department store, Lohman's livery stables, four saloons, two churches, a theater, a doctor's office, a grain elevator, and an assortment of stores selling ranching and farming equipment. But the most important place in town was the Great Northern station. The railroad was the lifeblood of the town. It connected Chinook to Havre and points west while providing the means to ship our crops and cattle to the big cities to the east. Chinook wouldn't exist without the Great Northern.

A week after my decision to live alone, Leo returned from Havre with a present. He had a large black dog to keep me company. I named him Buck and he became my constant companion. He would follow me to the barn, in the fields, and even when I walked across the prairie to the neighbors. Buck wasn't a handsome dog, but he was loyal and very protective. I felt much more secure at night knowing he would bark and alert to any strange noises.

Leo made some improvements to my place, in particular building shelves and painting my floors. I moved in with the Furchtbar's until he finished his work. In the meantime, Alma Tinker agreed to stay with me when both Father and Leo were away from the homestead. I still did not like staying alone.

After Leo finished the cupboards and floor my little house was quite comfortable. I put a picture of Mother on one wall and a picture of Grandmother Richmond on the other. My curtains were a bright pattern of flowers and I made a table-cloth to match. My bed was carefully made and covered with a colorful patch quilt Mother and I had stitched together. On the back wall was the stove, which could burn wood, coal, or dried cow dung if necessary. Finally, I had a nice little rocking chair to sit on either inside or outside. All in all, my shack was very homey.

Father hired a man to help around the place. We worked to make my homestead into a functioning ranch. I planted a large vegetable garden with peas, beans, tomatoes, carrots, and potatoes. George, the hired hand, and I planted flax, a very profitable crop in central Montana, on the ten acres I had cleared last fall. We also plowed thirty more acres, which would remain fallow this year and be ready for crops next spring. We improved the shelter for our horses and planted alfalfa and hay for the animals. When Papa returned from a business trip to eastern Montana, he and Leo started fencing the fields. The fence was made of spare posts from Father's construction sites and barbed wire. By the end of the summer they had strung up over a mile of fencing. The other significant improvement was the building of a chicken coop and a granary. Overall, I was feeling very proud of how my little ranch was coming along.

After a busy spring, Father drove a truck to the ranch to give me a big surprise. He had my piano.

"I knew you would want this now that your house is done," he said with a big smile. "Besides, it wasn't doing any good at my place."

"Oh Papa, thank you. I've been so busy I hadn't even thought about asking for the piano." I was excited as Father and Leo moved it into my house. We had to rearrange a bit, but it became the center of my living room. I started playing as soon as it was in place.

Our days went from dawn to dusk, but supper was often a community affair. Many evenings were spent either at Furchtbar's or at my place with Leo, Alma, and others coming for a meal and companionship against the isolation of the prairie. If we were at my house I would bring out my phonograph or play piano. We would sing and dance and laugh until we were exhausted. Many nights we would quietly curl up on the floor if we were at someone else's place. All in all, it was a happy, relaxed time.

Father continued to live in Havre, but he came out to the ranch at least once a week and usually stayed for a day or two. As the summer went on and I became more settled, his visits were shorter – usually a quick stop to deliver something or to bring me into town. He loved his Model T and would drive all around the county to show it off since there were very few automobiles in the area. He usually came on a Friday afternoon and it became our ritual to go to dances. He would pick up a group of us on the prairie and drive us to a dance in one of the neighboring communities, Cherry Ridge, Chinook, Harlem, or DuClair. We would go to the dance, sleep out in the open, then Father would drive us back to the homesteads the next morning. It was great fun.

We became masters of on-the-spot auto repairs, as breakdowns were frequent. I have many memories of helping Father fix flats – sometimes two or three on a single trip – getting out of mud holes, cooling the radiator, or even driving on the rims when the tires wore out. Twice the starter crank backfired and gave me huge bruises on my leg. Sometimes we had to leave the car and walk for miles until we met someone heading back toward the ranch. But we learned from each experience.

One day, in early April, a team of hired hands came through on their way to work at the Furchtbar place. The leader of the group was Harry Green, better known as "Red" due to the flame red color of his hair. He and his crew were making a good reputation in the area as the best field hands you could hire. On their way past my house Red came over and talked.

"Do you remember me from the line at the Land Office when you waited to file your claim?"

I laughed and said, "Of course, how could I miss your red hair? Good to see you again. Did you get a good claim?"

He looked around my place and over at the reservoir, "I didn't get as nice a plot as you, but I'm happy with what I've got. I'm about ten miles northeast of here in DuClair, closer to the Canadian border. It's good land and I'm doing okay."

I smiled. He was energetic, relaxed, and easy to talk to. "I've heard you do a good bit of helping out. I might be calling on you later, come harvest time."

He smiled back, "Well, I've got a strong team of horses, good work crew, and most folks around here can use the help. I can make an extra buck by helping plow, disc, or harvest. I like keeping busy."

"I'll keep it in mind," I said and he went on his way. I was impressed with his enthusiasm and willingness to do hard work. He seemed like a nice guy to have around.

One warm night Leo and I went hunting and, after shooting a couple of ducks by the pond, took them back to his shack for dinner. After dinner we sat outside watching a beautiful red sunset. As it was getting dark we talked about our life on the prairie.

"I love it out here," I said. "I feel so free and relaxed. I don't always have to dress properly, get up at an expected time, or have my hair done just right. I loved Mama's instructions of how to be a lady, but I don't miss the unending attention to detail and the demands to always look my best. I am starting to enjoy the prairie more than the city. I can ride my horse whenever and wherever I want. I like getting my hands dirty, doing hard work, and not depending on anyone – man or woman – to get it done. Life on the prairie has taught me a lot. It's toughened me up."

"Yes," Leo said, "You have changed from the proper young lady I met three years ago. Back then you were uptight and careful about everything you said and did. I still see that side of you when we are in town, but out here you are a different woman. When you first came to town you were quiet and allowed your parents to make decisions for you. Out here you make the decisions and you are in charge. You are tougher and want to do the work. You are a different woman."

"Yes, I am," I said, as I looked at Leo to try to read his thoughts. "Is it okay with you? Is it a good change?"

He hesitated a bit in thought, then said, "Of course. I love seeing you unafraid to live on your own and do the work. We went hunting this afternoon and you did not depend on me to shoot the ducks. You got your own."

Before I could question him more, he changed the subject. "There is one thing I've noticed though."

"What?" I asked.

"You don't like being alone in the dark."

I laughed. "You are so right. There are too many things out at night. The coyotes, bobcats, snakes, and rough terrain can all trip you up. Yes – I don't like being alone out here in the dark."

Leo chuckled and said, "Well – we are going to get rid of your fears tonight."

"What do you mean? What do you have in mind?"

"I want you to walk to your house and back without a light. You must make it by the light of the moon and your own instincts."

Suddenly I was scared. I did not like the idea but did not want to show Leo my fear. "Will you be watching me?" was all I said.

"Yes, I will watch you the whole way."

So I set off on my never-to-be-forgotten walk in the moonlight. After the first tentative steps I realized it was a wonderful, beautiful night. Coyotes howling in the distance startled me, but I realized they were a long way off and their howls became more musical to me. I walked to the hills, then down to my house. It was rather spooky entering my house and feeling around for a match to light the kerosene lamp. But I did it and realized I had more courage for having done it. Leo and I laughed about it for the next two days.

Leo and I went back to Havre for Easter week. It was a very busy time with an endless stream of events. I was God-mother at a baptism, went to Easter services with Father, and attended an Easter party at the Lyceum Hall. Leo and I went to a movie at the Orpheum, danced at the Elks Club, and I attended a meeting of the Music Club. In between all those events we ate, chatted with friends, and played cards. By the end of the week I couldn't wait to get back to the ranch and relax a bit.

Getting back to the ranch was more of an adventure than most trips. Alma joined us on the return so the car was loaded down with people and bags. Father's car broke down halfway to Chinook, so while he worked to repair it, Alma, Leo, and I caught a freight train to Chinook, and then hitched a ride out to the ranch on a hay wagon. It took the whole day to get there, but when we got to my little home we all laughed about what a crazy day it had been.

The end of May marked the first anniversary of Mother's death, so I went back to Havre for a week with Father. It was a terrible time for both of us in many ways. I was irritable and, as a result, Leo and I had a huge argument over nothing. It was a continuation of an on-and-off again discussion of our relationship, our feelings for each other, and our equal desire to be independent and dominant. He didn't talk to me for four days, but the timing was significant because I needed his support more than at any other time. Father returned from a hunting trip with a bug bite we couldn't identify. It became infected and caused blood poisoning. He had to be watched and cared for constantly, much to his chagrin. Emotionally, both of us were a wreck.

Although we tried to distract ourselves with other activities neither of us could get our minds off the events of Mother's death and funeral. On June second, the anniversary of her funeral, I cleaned house, played bridge, made supper for Father and friends, yet still cried myself to sleep after writing a diary entry. "A year ago today Mama was laid to rest in Melrose. I recall every minute of the horrible day – I cannot write about it." Again I promised to be the woman Mother wanted me to be.

A Loss and a Change: 1914

When I returned to the ranch Leo came over and we talked. He apologized for his earlier anger and we made up. Our fights were becoming more frequent and usually the cause was determined to be silly and insignificant. I could not get a handle on our relationship. I knew I loved him, and he said he loved me, but something seemed to be missing and we weren't able to build a closer relationship. We had different religions, family backgrounds, and occupational desires. We discussed those issues often but did not make any decisions to bring us closer to a mutual agreement.

The crisis came to a head in the middle of June. Leo had gone into Havre and had been away for a week on railroad business. I hadn't felt well for over a month and was experiencing an unusual amount of cramping. My monthly cycle didn't come on time, and I was an emotional wreck. I couldn't take it any longer and had to talk to someone.

"Alma, I don't feel good." Alma Tinker, my neighbor to the south, had been staying with me while Father and Leo were away. Neither of us liked staying alone, so it worked well. As a matter of fact, I didn't know how Alma was going to prove up her claim since you were required to physically be on your land for seven months. She had not stayed at her place for more than two or three days at a time since she built it. She was either in town visiting or staying with neighbors on the prairie. But since we were both single women, she had become a close friend and confidante.

"What's wrong Mabel?" she asked.

"I can't seem to keep food down. I eat and then throw up, especially in the morning. It's not like me at all."

Alma looked at me with a perplexed look. "You get sick in the mornings? Have you and Leo been – well, you know – together? Could you be pregnant?"

Her question shocked me. Not because she asked it, or even that she might suspect Leo and I were having relations. We had been together on occasion, but it was not a frequent event. Leo and I never talked about it. I had not even thought about the possibility of being pregnant. I had always tried to do the right thing, and had sworn I would not have relations with anyone until I was married, but it had happened, and now I might be suffering the consequences.

I didn't know how to answer Alma. "Pregnant? No, I don't think so ... but maybe ... God, I don't know. Oh – that's scary. I hadn't thought ..."

Alma looked at me and asked bluntly, "Have you and Leo ...? Would he be the father?"

"Yes. But only a couple of times. Oh, this is so embarrassing. Please – you can't tell anyone. Please promise me you won't tell anyone. I can't go to town. I can't go anywhere. What will people think? Please, please, don't say anything. I don't want to talk about it any more. I'll have to wait and see." I was worried Alma would tell someone. She was a good friend, but a bit of a gossip.

"I promise," said Alma. "I'll protect your secret for now and help as you get further along. Sooner or later you are going to have to tell Leo and your father. You can't keep it a secret from them."

"Oh, I know. But I don't want anyone else to know until I'm sure and until I talk to Leo and Father. God – Papa will be furious. I know he cannot imagine his little girl getting pregnant – especially out of wedlock. He'll go after Leo to marry me right away. There will be more arguments. Nothing good will come out of this." As I thought of the future possibilities, I started crying.

Alma asked, "What will Leo do? Doesn't he want to marry you? Won't he do the right thing and admit it is his and marry you?"

Tears were streaming down my face. "I'm not sure what Leo will do. He has told me many times he isn't ready to get married, but maybe this baby will change his mind. I don't want to trick him into getting married. He likes his job and doesn't want to move out of the city. He got his land because of me, but he doesn't especially like it out here on the prairie. And the bigger issue is his parents. They say they will only allow him to marry another Catholic. They like me, but won't condone our marriage if I'm not Catholic. I can't imagine what they will say when they hear I'm pregnant. Oh my, there is just too much to think about. I can't do it. Please, Alma, help me figure this out. What should I do?"

I think Alma enjoyed being the sole person in the know. "I'm here for you. I'll keep the secret. You'll be alright."

It was summer, so there was plenty to do around the ranch to keep busy. I tended my garden, cleaned the house, checked the grain in the fields for bugs and disease, and cared for the animals. Leo returned a week later. By then I was sure I was pregnant.

"Leo, dear, we have to talk," I said as we sat in the house having a cup of tea.

He could tell it was something serious. "Of course. What's on your mind?"

There was no subtle way to tell him, so I quickly blurted it out, "I'm pregnant."

Leo looked away in disbelief. He started to talk, stopped, smiled, then frowned. He was lost for words.

"Remember the night in May?" I said.

"Of course I do. How could I forget? But we said we weren't going to talk about it. I thought everything was okay. I didn't think this would happen. God – it was ... I mean it's wonderful, but ..." And his voice trailed off as he held his head.

"Aren't you happy? Aren't you excited? You look like you're not happy about this. We can get married and everything will be fine." I was hoping for a different reaction from him. I suddenly thought he wasn't happy or in love with me.

He recovered a bit and realized he wasn't being supportive. "Of course, I'm happy and excited. Of course, we will get married. But you caught me off guard. I'm just totally surprised. I'm trying to digest the whole thing. Have you told anyone else? Does your father know?"

"Alma knows. She was the one who realized I was pregnant last week. But I haven't told anyone else and Alma promised not to say anything until I talked to you and Papa. I haven't told him yet. He hasn't been home – he's off on another hunting trip to the mountains and probably won't be home for three or four days. That will give us time to make plans and prepare for his obvious reaction."

Leo looked nervous. "Yes – I'm not looking forward to that discussion. Nor do I want to tell my mother. She will be furious and it will all be my fault."

"Father will be all right. He likes you. His biggest concern will be to ensure we do everything correctly so it doesn't damage his name and reputation. What do you think your mother will say?"

"She is still insisting I can't marry outside the faith. And the possibility of an illegitimate child who isn't Catholic will send her to the priest right away. I'll be forced to make penance for years."

Leo continued. When he was upset he would just talk, ask questions, and not wait for an answer. "Ed is worried about his name and reputation? What about mine? What about yours? Does he only care about himself?"

"Sometimes I think so. But let's talk about our baby," I said as I rubbed my stomach. "What should we do? Get married before I start showing too much? Get married out here or in town? What do you think?"

Leo shook his head. "I don't know. This is all too quick. I need time to think things through. Can we talk about this later?" Leo always put off problems and difficult decisions.

I didn't want to put it off, and Leo's attitude upset me. "Are you saying we shouldn't get married? Don't you want to marry me? Would your mother actually prohibit a marriage, even to the woman you love who is carrying your baby? You're a grown man. Are you still doing everything your mother wants? Why can't you make your own decisions and live your own life?"

"Of course, I can make my own decisions. But can you imagine how bitter it's going to be and how tough it will be whenever we see family? I'm not sure I'm ready for the rejection. I love my family – my brothers and sisters are very close to me – and I don't want to be cut off from them."

I was so frustrated I started to cry. "This is going nowhere. You haven't answered any of my questions about us and our future."

Leo looked dejected, discouraged, and confused. "I can't answer your questions right now. I must have time to think. I don't mean to hurt you, but I can't handle it all right now. Please give me some time to digest this. I've got to go."

I was furious. "Where are you going? You can't turn your back on me. We've got to discuss this. Do you want to marry me or not?"

"Yes, I want to marry you, but not under these circumstances. I don't like being forced into anything."

I was trying my best to remain calm and rational, but it was getting harder and harder. "Well, you can't change it. It is what it is, so you'd better decide what you're going to do."

After a couple minutes of silence Leo finally said, "Yes, you are right. I have to accept this. I will marry you, but let's wait until we tell Edmond and my mother before we set any dates or finalize things."

I was relieved. "Thank you. We can do that."

Two days later Father came home and we told him right away. He was instantly furious and I thought he was going to hit Leo, but then he calmed down.

"You are going to marry her aren't you?" he asked looking at Leo.

"Yes sir," said Leo. "I will do the right thing, but we haven't set any date or place or anything. We wanted to tell you and my mother first."

Still, Leo remained vague and noncommittal. I found it disturbing but figured things would change in time. His mother reacted as he had predicted, rambling on about how sinful her son was, what a wicked woman I was, and how the whole family would be embarrassed to attend church. It was insulting and disturbing that she could see a pregnancy as a sinful situation. I could not understand her logic.

A week later our little prairie community had a Fourth of July celebration at the Slonaker's ranch. Their place was about a quarter mile from mine. Elmer and Bessie had invited everyone over for dinner and an evening together. Father was off on a business trip for a couple weeks so Leo and I went alone. We felt it was too early to announce my pregnancy since I was only about eight weeks and wasn't showing yet. We asked Alma not to say anything.

The party was great fun. I brought over my phonograph and played records. We ate roast chicken and duck, potatoes, vegetables, and a berry pie for dessert. Throughout the afternoon I doted on the Slonaker's two babies. They were so cute and I kept thinking how I could soon play with my own. Being an only child, I did not have younger siblings to care for or play with and had always wanted a large family. Now I started dreaming of how great it would be with four or five children to love and care for.

We sang and danced and watched the fireworks Elmer had brought from Great Falls. It was after midnight when Leo and I headed home. On our walk across the prairie I commented on how much fun I had with the babies. I was feeling good and didn't notice Leo's silence and surly mood.

"It will be so wonderful to have our own child to care for and love. I'm so excited about getting married and having this baby," I said.

119

Leo looked at me without saying anything.

"Why the silence? I know you – there's something on your mind. Let's not fight tonight, please."

Leo let out a big sigh. "I don't want to fight. But this gathering made me realize we must come to a solution soon. We need to tell our friends about the baby."

"Oh yes. I agree. We should discuss our wedding plans tomorrow so we can start telling everyone." I thought this was what Leo was trying to say.

"Mabel, dear, I don't know how to say this. I know you are going to get upset, but I don't think I can marry you."

I stopped in my tracks and looked at him. "What? Why would you say that?"

"I have too many hesitations. I watched the Slonakers all night. They are a beautiful couple with a nice family, but I can't see myself in that position. I know we've been together for a while now, but I can't leave my job and come out here full time. I am not a farmer. I'm not ready for marriage and children. I know you will hate me, but it's the honest truth."

For a minute I just stood there, too shocked to say anything. "You don't want to marry me? You don't even want to acknowledge your child? How can you say that? How can you pretend this was all for fun? We've been over and over the issue of you staying with the railroad. We've talked about where we will live. You're only using those things as an excuse to not marry me. You say you love me, but I don't believe you. Right now I don't know what to say. Get out of my sight. I don't want to see you. You've ruined a perfect evening. Get out of here."

He left. The next morning he went into town without saying good-bye.

For two days I stayed in my shack and cried. Buck was the only company I had. He sensed something was wrong and stayed close to me, but of course, he didn't provide the answers I needed. I had never been so miserable and had no idea what I was going to do next in my life. Alma came for a visit and I told her everything. She tried to help, but I couldn't be consoled. I sent her away.

The next day changed my life. The cramps came suddenly in the morning. I was doubled up with stomach and back pain for hours. Then the bleeding started. I was alone, scared, and in a bit of shock. I realized I was losing the baby and by the end of the day there was no doubt. When I thought I could not take another moment of pain, our baby, my baby, left my body.

I'll never know why I lost the baby. It could have been a number of factors. It could have been God's way of telling me something, but I didn't see it. I've always felt it was from the stress of my relationship with Leo and fears of losing him.

I was exhausted, in pain, and alone. I felt ugly and rejected by the man I loved. I cried for hours. I cleaned up as best I could but was so very tired, both physically and emotionally, I felt sleep close in on me and I was thankful to leave the pain and emotional hurt behind.

I slept most of the next day. Each time I awoke my heart filled with loneliness and despair for the loss of my baby and Leo. In those moments I didn't feel I could ever forgive him or return to the love we had previously enjoyed.

In the evening Bessie Slonaker came over and found me still in bed and an emotional wreck. When she came in she said, "You haven't been out and around like you usually are, and I didn't see Leo either. My senses told me something was wrong." It was time to tell her everything. I told her about my pregnancy, the fight, and Leo's leaving.

Bessie took the small fetus, wrapped in it a clean cloth, and we had a small, quiet burial in the back of my house. She made some tea and washed my dirty, bloody clothes and sheets. I was glad she had come over. Bessie was a sweet soul and her instincts were strong. She had experienced childbirth and was much more logical and down-to-earth than Alma. She sat with me and made me talk out my troubles. It helped, but I still felt I would never survive the devastation that over-whelmed me.

"My heart goes out to you Mabel and I am so sorry for the loss of your little one, but you can overcome this. Miscar-riages happen and those we love can disappoint us, but your family and friends are here to take care of you. Everyone in our community loves you. We won't let you go down this road alone. Try to stay positive." Bessie said everything I needed to hear.

"You are right. I can recover from this. I'm not going to let this get me down," I agreed after we had talked for an hour or so. "I have to be strong. I have to keep moving on. Mother always told me to not look back, look forward. I'm not the first woman to lose a baby. I can keep going. I will make my own life." The more I talked about it, the better I felt.

"What about Leo?" Bessie asked. "Are you going to see him again?"

"I'm going to wait and see. He abandoned me in my greatest time of need. That's not good. I don't understand him sometimes. He can be loving and romantic, but whenever there is any pressure on him about marriage or commitment, he runs away and always has some excuse. He will blame work, or his mother, or his sisters, or something else. I thought I loved him – I do still love him – but I can't quite understand him. I've got to sort it all out. It's too confusing right now. I'll have to see what he says and does when, and if, he comes back. I'm not going to run to him."

"Do you want me to tell him you lost the baby?" Bessie asked.

I thought for a moment. "Let's wait a while. I want to see if he will come back without knowing I've lost the baby." I looked at Bessie. She was so calm and reassuring under pressure. "You're a good friend – my best friend. Thank you for being here. Thank you for helping."

She laughed. "Mabel, out here if we don't take care of each other and aren't honest with each other, we will all die. We've got to be one big family."

I realized she was right. Friendship was the key to survival on the prairie.

Leo returned to the ranch a week later. I saw the light on at his cabin, but he didn't get the nerve to come over for two more days. When he did, he hesitantly approached the house, knowing I was watching him.

"Hello Mabel. I did a lot of thinking while I was in town and I realized I was being stupid and immature. I'm as responsible for this as you are. I have to accept what's happened and marry you. It's the right thing to do. We've talked a lot about marriage – I don't know why I have been so hesitant. I need to step up and be a man about all this."

I didn't want to let him off too easily and I was a bit concerned about what he would say about losing the baby. "Thank you. I'm happy you finally want to accept some responsibility for my pregnancy," I said quietly. "But there has been a change. I'm no longer pregnant. I miscarried and lost the baby last week."

His look showed confusion, but also concern. "You mean you aren't going to have a baby? What happened? Are you okay? Will you be able to have children in the future?" Suddenly he realized he had left something out. "Oh – I'm so sorry. I should have been here for you. You had to do it all by yourself. I'm sorry."

"Yes, I did have to do it all myself. And yes, I'm okay." I looked at him, trying to read his mind. "I did a lot of thinking too. Thinking about me and you and what I want to do. And I've come to a decision. I don't know if you are going to like it, but it's what I'm going to do, so you'll have to accept it."

"Okay, I can understand you had time to think about things. Whatever your decision – I will accept it."

"I want to continue seeing you, but only as good friends. I still love you, but I think we need to discuss some things – like marriage, family, lifestyles, and all the things that have been dividing us. Do you understand?" I was scared of what Leo's reaction would be. I had to keep talking. "Can we be friends – still help each other, still go to dances and parties together, still laugh and cry together? This baby thing really scared me. Not only the pregnancy part, but I thought I was going to lose you. I want to be your wife, but not until we get everything figured out. Do you agree?"

He looked at me and broke out in a big smile. "I love you," was all he said. Then he laughed and went on, "I wasn't sure what I was going to say when I came over. I wanted to continue seeing you too. I was afraid I might lose you and didn't know what I could do to get you back. I should have known you would have the answer. Yes, I will be your best friend. Didn't your mother always say to 'turn the page' to the next chapter? Well – I'm ready to go to the next chapter. Let's see what it has together." He reached over to take my hand and I grabbed him and gave him a big hug.

It was time for a new chapter.

We agreed to not look back, which meant we would not even talk about my pregnancy and miscarriage. We emphasized our desires to move forward to Father, Alma, and Bessie. Leo told his parents, and his mother was relieved. They all understood and promised to help. I even decided to cut the pages out of my diary where I had written of the pregnancy and my feelings about it. I had made some very bitter and angry entries and did not want a record of any of it. I needed to forget the events from June eleventh to July sixteenth, so those pages were fed to the fire. As I watched the pages burn I felt closure to an ugly episode in my life. I felt I could move on without any record of that terrible month.

One entry, in particular, was painful to write and I never wanted to read it again. I had written, "What would Mother say? She would be so disappointed in me. She raised me to be a lady and be proud of myself. But now I am pregnant and don't want to go out in public. It will be such an embarrassment. I'm so sorry Mama – I have failed to live up to your expectations."

Once more I promised to make Mama proud of me. I would be the intelligent, strong, independent, and loving woman she wanted.

Ranching and Politics on the High Plains

Leo went back to Havre for work and I didn't see him for almost a month. Although I missed him it felt good to be working on my own. I thought about how much I had learned and matured since I moved to the homestead. I worked the fields, tended the horses, milked the cows, fed the chickens, and took care of the house. Alma Tinker and Bessie Slonaker visited often to keep me company and help out. Bessie's husband, Elmer, and James Furchtbar helped with some of the heavy lifting, and Father came out, usually on weekends, and did what he could. Weekend trips to dances and parties became less frequent and ranch work took a new precedence.

It was an unusually hot summer with extended temperatures in the nineties. The thermometer topped one hundred degrees for three straight days in late July. We were all concerned about water. The spring rains decreased to minimal showers, and when it did rain, the wind came up and quickly evaporated whatever water remained on the soil. I had been unable to do much in the fields during my short pregnancy and the crops suffered due to the lack of attention. They were stunted and weeks behind their normal growth. The reservoir shrunk and we were afraid to irrigate too much for fear of losing the pond altogether. We tried digging the well deeper, but after going down over ten feet we still had little to show for our work.

Occasionally Papa would say or do something that demonstrated his lack of farming experience. In the midst of this dry spell Father had an unusual suggestion. "Mabel, we need to create a fire break around your house. As dry as it is out here you should be concerned about a wildfire starting with a lightning strike. If we have a controlled burn we can clear out an area and keep you safe."

"But Papa, isn't it too dry?" I asked.

Father insisted. "Not if we are here to watch it. We can control what happens. I think it needs to be done."

So, on one of the hottest days of the year, we deliberately started a fire on the east side of the house. Suddenly the wind shifted, sparks jumped fifteen to twenty feet, and in less than five minutes it seemed as if the whole county were ablaze. We fought like fiends to get it under control but to little avail. Every time we put the fire out in one place a spark would fly across the prairie and start a flare up in another spot. At one point the flames were within a few feet of my house before the wind swirled around and blew it away from the house. Only when our neighbors showed up with their hired hands were we able to put the fire out. It was frightening and careless of us. Father was very embarrassed and apologized to the other men. It cured him of making recommendations for the ranch.

Ironically, two days later it started to rain. It rained steadily for the next four days. The coulees filled up, the trails and dirt roads turned to a muddy quagmire, and we couldn't venture outside except for the most essential of chores. Many of the low-lying ranches suffered damage from flash floods as the water ran off the hard packed ground in great torrents. I was safe from flooding as Father had selected the perfect spot for my house. I still had a number of leaks and had to move everything to the middle of the house as puddles formed in all the low areas of the floor and worked feverishly to keep my piano dry. It was hard work, but I was successful. When the rain stopped the reservoir was full again and my well had adequate water pressure. The crops had suffered greatly, first from the drought, then with the excess rain beating them down to the ground. We feared we would not have much of a harvest. Only time would tell as the summer went on.

The whole community worked together, but it still took over a week to clean up our homes. We started at Leo's, since it was the smallest around. We had to wash all his clothes, wash the floor and his cupboards, and dry out the hay he had stored for his animals. My house was a mess. My clothes, dishes, stored food, cupboards, and floor were all soaked. Everything had to be washed then moved outside to dry. Luck was with us, as we had a good week of sunny days.

On August tenth Leo came out to the prairie with big news. "War has started in Europe. England, France, and Russia are at war with Germany and Austria-Hungary. It started last week when Germany invaded Belgium. I heard about it at the Great Northern dispatch office and read it in the paper the other day. The Crown Prince of Austria-Hungary was assassinated a couple weeks ago and the Austrians blamed Serbia. Russia promised to help Serbia and Germany promised to help Austria. Suddenly all of Europe is at war. It doesn't sound good."

I was shocked. We rarely heard news from Europe out on the prairie, so I knew it was bad. "The U.S. isn't getting involved, is it?" I asked.

"No. President Wilson has emphasized to the press we are a neutral nation and will continue to trade with all the nations of Europe. He doesn't want to get involved in the fighting. He says we have too many friends and business interests on both sides. He says it's a European affair."

"Thank God," I said. "I have German friends back in Minnesota who will be very upset if we go to war against their homeland. I'm sure they are hoping for a quick German victory. I don't want any American boys to go overseas to fight someone else's war. We have nothing to do with this and should stay out of it."

Leo looked at me and smiled. "I knew you would have a quick, strong opinion. There is apparently a lot going on, but if we can stay out of it and keep shipping grain overseas it should be good for business."

Late August and early September was harvest time. The golden fields of wheat rippled in the wind waiting to be cut and threshed. The flax seeds and oats hung heavy on their stalks. The air took on the smell of crisp freshness with the approaching autumn, mixed with the smell of fresh cut grains. No other time of the year was as busy or strenuous, but it was also the time of year when the prairie community came to-gether to get the work done. All the men and boys worked in the fields from sunup to sundown. In addition to the local residents, additional help was usually brought in. Everyone would get up early, have a big breakfast before daylight, then head to the fields. The women would get together to cook a big midday meal and take it to the field to feed the men. Work went on until it was too dark to see. Then it was repeated again the next day until all the crops were brought in. When one person's fields were done everyone would move to the next homestead. It was a time of cooperation, togetherness, and hard work.

Harry "Red" Green and his crew were everywhere during the harvest season. Red had a strong eight horse team and an experienced crew of six other men who could thresh and clear the fields faster than anyone in the county, so they were in high demand. The Slonakers, Furchtbars, Crofts, Ovesens, and Robertsons all had large acreage of grain and hired Red's crew to help with their harvest. The only major landholder in the area who did not hire Red and his crew was Mr. Harbolt, who had his own men. He didn't socialize with the other families and always had his own way of doing things.

Since I didn't have much acreage to harvest and didn't have a husband working with the threshers, my fields were going to be harvested later. I helped with the cooking and enjoyed the camaraderie. The evening meal would be well after dark when the day's work was done and everything was cleaned up. Usually, the families went back to their respective homes, but since Red's crew was miles from home and would be expected back in the fields at sunrise, they camped wherever they were working. They were on their own for their evening meals. One morning Red brought a couple chickens over to my place.

"Good morning, Miss Richmond," he said. "My team is working over at Robertson's today and Mr. Robertson said you are the best cook in the area. Would you cook these up for my crew and we'll come back at suppertime?" He looked so helpless I could not say no.

That night Red and his crew sat outside my shack and ate chicken, potatoes, beans, and berry pie. After the meal I played piano for the men. They laughed and sang and we had a great time until late into the night. Red had a beautiful singing voice and would lead his crew in the songs. He was always the center of attention, had a myriad of stories to tell, and loved playing practical jokes on the men of his crew. They were sleeping in Mr. Robertson's equipment shed, so were in no hurry to leave my place. As the night went on, Red thanked me for their supper. "The meal was delicious, Miss Richmond. We will be at Robertson's for a couple more days. If I bring you more chickens, would you cook for us again? We'll gladly pay you for your efforts."

"First of all, call me Mabel," I said laughing. "I'm glad to cook for you and your men. You are great company and work hard. You don't need to pay me. I enjoy doing it," I said, smiling.

"Well, maybe we could do some work around your place in exchange for your cooking. I don't mean to be rude, but your fields could use a little attention. I'd be glad to help."

He was big, strong, and nonstop motion. I couldn't resist his offer. "I don't have a huge field, but yes, I could use some help." With the miscarriage, drought, excessive rain, and my own inexperience, my crops were in bad shape, especially the flax, which was my main cash crop. I was afraid I wouldn't have any to harvest in the fall.

For the next week I cooked for Red and his crew every day and they came over for supper, music, and laughter. When they finished at Robertson's they came to my place. Red walked the fields and came back and reported, "Your flax doesn't look good. It is nowhere near ready to harvest, and to be honest, Mabel, I don't think it's going to make it. We can cut and bale your hay and bring in some alfalfa, but that's about all we can do for now."

I was disappointed but appreciated his honesty. I wasn't planning much profit from the flax, but I was worried about being able to prove up for the year. The homestead rules were vague but said I needed a crop to have a good year. "That's fine. Do you think I will have enough crop to file my proof for this year?"

Red looked out at my fields. "I don't really know. The Homestead rules say you should have about twenty acres under cultivation. You've got about forty acres plowed up. Most of it is fallow, but I don't know if that counts or not."

"It will help if you can bring in the hay and alfalfa. I'll have to take my chances. I'm sure I'm not the only one around here who had problems with the drought."

It only took Red's crew two days to cut my hay and alfalfa, which was much quicker than I could have done it. I was convinced I got the best part of the deal. Red and his men were always gentlemen and well behaved. I was impressed.

As they packed their gear and prepared for the next farm, Red stopped over. "Mabel, I enjoyed your cooking. You take care and I'll check back later to see if you need help plowing and preparing for next year. Think you might be interested in renting out some of your land?"

"Thank you for your hard work," I said. "Yes, I might be interested in renting some land. It would work out well for both of us." We agreed to talk about it later and he moved on to another farm.

A few weeks later he and his crew returned and helped me plow, disc, and plant my winter crops. With their help I was able to clear more land and plant almost forty acres of flax for next year. With any luck I would make up for this year's disaster. I also agreed to rent Red twenty acres for him to work.

Everyone in our little community had great respect for Red Green. He was tall – almost six feet – strong, and energetic. He was polite, kind, and helpful to all. He could be boisterous and self-confident, but he backed up his ego with his work and friendliness. He always had a smile on his face. I especially liked his personality and hardworking attitude. Also, he sang while he worked, which I found especially pleasing. Nothing ever seemed to be too big an obstacle for him. As time went on he became a trusted friend, which was always important on the High Plains.

The war in Europe continued to be news. Whenever an article appeared in the local newspapers we would share the news with everyone, but the major political issue in Montana was much more personal and closer to home. Montana was voting on a proposal to give women the right to vote in November, and this was important to me. If I wanted to be an independent woman, I needed to have a say in the politics of our state and nation. I was strongly in favor of the proposal, much to Father's and Leo's chagrin.

In early October Alma and I attended a gathering in Havre and heard Margaret Smith Hathaway give an impassioned speech supporting women's suffrage. I was in awe of her speaking ability, her bravery, and her logical arguments. After the meeting we all marched through Havre with signs demanding the right to vote. It was intoxicating to be a small part of the movement. I had to convince Father and Leo to vote yes.

At first Leo resisted my pressure to support the measure, but when his four sisters joined the discussion he conceded and said he would vote yes. He realized he would be giving us all more political influence and independence. Father, unfortunately, was another matter.

"I will not vote for such a stupid proposal. Period!" He was shouting at me. "A woman's place is in the home and her husband will decide the politics of the household. That's the way it has always been. Every man at the Elks is going to vote no – I can guarantee it. Your mother would be ashamed of you marching through the streets of Havre like a loose woman."

"No, Father, I disagree. Mother would be proud of me." I surprised myself by standing up to my father. "She raised me to be courageous and freethinking. This is the biggest thing to impact women in a long time. I think she would be marching right next to me. She was stronger than you think. Mother would want you to vote yes for my sake. Think of it – I'm single and out on the prairie doing what many consider a man's work. Shouldn't I have a say in what's going on in this state? Shouldn't I be able to vote on laws affecting me as a property owner? You taught me to shoot. You stood in line for me so I could get the property. You supported my actions out there. Why can't you support my having the right to vote?" By using Mother as an example I knew I was pulling on his emotions, but he was stubborn.

"Those are all good arguments," he said in a rare compliment, "but it isn't going to change anything. I'm still voting no. I'm not going to be the only man in Hill County to vote yes on this thing. I wouldn't be able to face my brothers at the Elks or the Masons. So stop this chatter right now."

In November the proposal passed in the statewide voting. It failed in Blaine County, which had a high population of single male homesteaders, but in Hill County, where Havre was, it passed by a slim majority. I discovered Father voted for passage of the bill. "Don't tell anyone, but you convinced me Mabel. I voted yes, but I'm not talking about it and I'm going to deny voting yes if anyone at the Elks or Masons asks me. So don't go bragging about how your father voted. Hear?"

I was so proud of him. He had swallowed his pride and listened to me. I gave him a big hug and said, "Thank you Papa. You gave me the right to vote. That is so wonderful. Your secret is safe with me."

I still was not comfortable staying alone in my shack for extended periods of time. The silence of the prairie at night tortured my imagination. I would lay in bed and hear noises. The coyotes howl and the movement of the horses and cattle would rattle me. Maybe it was just the wind blowing through the grasses or a rattle from the barn, but it worked on my nerves and kept me awake. My dog, Buck, was good company and would alert when there were strange noises, but he was not human. I needed conversation.

I wanted a neighbor to stay with me as much as possible. Alma Tinker was my most frequent guest, but I often spent the night at Furchtbars' or Crofts'. One evening was especially scary. Alma came to my cabin late at night paralyzed with fear. She had seen two men she didn't recognize in her field. The next morning we discovered it was only two "tumbleweeds" looking for odd jobs. My diary was full of entries such as, "I hated to stay alone … it's so beastly lonely without Leo … I'm timid about being so far from anyone," and "I had to face a long Sunday afternoon alone."

Leo and I had been together more since our problems in July. He had been gone for almost a month after my miscarriage but returned to his ranch at harvest time. He was still my most trusted friend and we still had strong feelings for each other, but since the summer incident we had been less romantic and more cautious in our relationship. He had planted very little so his fall harvest tasks were simple and only required a couple weeks' work at the ranch. I was still in love with him and missed him when he wasn't near. In September we celebrated our fourth year together with a simple dinner at my cabin and a lovely night sitting outside looking at the stars. Afterward, I wrote in my diary, "This is our fourth anniversary. I wonder if another couple in the world has had such perfect happiness. We both have tempers, but our love is big enough to make little 'spats' only trivial. We've had much happiness and one great sorrow to bind us inseparably."

Of course, the "one great sorrow" was my short pregnancy and the subsequent damage to our relationship.

Shortly after an event occurred which had great impact on my relationship with Leo. His parents moved to Fort Benton, Montana. Leo had been raised in Havre and was very emotional about his parents moving and selling the family home. He felt like his home was being broken up. I was upset, too. The Delorimier family had become good friends, despite our religious differences, and I had many pleasant memories of visits to their home. I would soon discover this move would impact my future more than I could ever imagine.

Complications: 1915

In early November I moved back to my little house in Havre for the winter and resumed my winter social schedule. During the day I played bridge, sewed, and cooked for Father and his friends. Leo and I still went to all the evening dinners, dances, and parties, but during the day he was spending more time at the Great Northern office. He received a promotion and was now the manager of the dispatch office, which gave him increased responsibilities and demanded more of his time. Our time together became shorter and less regular.

Thanksgiving, Christmas, and New Year's came and went. The winter seemed to drag on and I became anxious to return to the ranch. I was surprised how much I missed the solitude and hard work of the homestead. I thought about it every day. One diary entry from early February sums up my feelings, "I am lonely for the old ranch and can't stand the city masses. The cement walks tire me and I can't get used to having to eat at regular hours. I love my old ranch not because I <u>have</u> to, but because I <u>do</u>." The realization city life was not for me and the need for some ready cash led me to sell my house in Havre. Havre was continuing to grow and an organization called The Home Builders Investment Company was buying up houses. They offered a fair price. I sold and didn't look back.

A warm spell came in the middle of March and I immediately wanted to get back to my homestead. On April eighth Papa and I drove back out to the ranch. The ground was still wet and we got stuck twice. We also had two flat tires, but it was all worthwhile when we pulled up outside my little place in the evening. Everything was still in place. It was cold, damp, and dusty, but it was all mine. I fired up the stove, started cleaning, and in no time was cozy and comfortable. I loved it.

In the spring the High Plains of Montana could be hypnotizing and enchanting with their own special beauty. The skies were endless with brilliant blues punctuated by great, white, fluffy clouds. The air was crisp and clear. The views were spectacular and more than my eyes take in in one glance. The land was a profusion of colors, smells, and visual treats. Flowers and grasses bloomed everywhere you looked. Red wild poppies, yellow buttercups, purple lupine, and bitterroot, accented by the white of the small woodland start, created a natural bouquet of beauty. The grasses had the light green of early shoots and the cottonwoods by the streams quickly blossomed. Bees were everywhere doing their best to get to every bit of pollen before it blew away in the steady winds. Fawns and young antelope scampered across the grasslands. To me, it was the most beautiful place on earth.

But the prairie could also be deadly. The vastness and unending space could overwhelm and disorient you in a second. The weather could change suddenly and violent storms of rain, cold, and wind came without warning. Then, suddenly, it could become unbearably hot and dry. Crops could be severely damaged or destroyed by hail and wind, or dried up from drought. And then there were the insects.

"Grasshoppers coming," was the panicked cry of a young man as he rode up to my house. "Coming from the south. They are closing in on the Robertson place. They need your help." Then he hurried on to the next farmstead to spread the alarm. Leo rode over with a shovel and old blanket. I grabbed my shovel, hopped on my horse, and we were off to help.

Grasshoppers were a huge problem in the spring. They loved the new growth and could chomp through hundreds of acres in ten to twelve hours. There was no guaranteed method to get rid of them. As we rode up to the Robertson place we could see them on the southern edge of his fields. It was an ugly black cloud of insects stretching for almost a quarter mile. All the neighbors were there trying their best to stomp on, sweep up, or crush the green devils. We all knew the hoppers wouldn't be satisfied with Robertsons' fields. Your place could be next. It seemed futile. Every bug killed seemed to be replaced by two or three more. The chirping noise and whir of their wings made a screeching, loud, eerie buzzing that was deafening. After over two hours of desperate attempts to stop the eating, Mr. Robertson decided on the most drastic solution.

"Nothing's working. We'll have to burn them out," he yelled over the commotion.

"But that will mean the destruction of your crop," someone responded.

"I know – but it's got to be done. If we don't stop them here they will keep going to my north field, then over to yours and everyone else. We've got to do it." Robertson was depressed and frustrated, but he knew he would have to sacrifice his south field to save everyone else.

We all went to our own places to gather oil and kerosene then quickly returned to the Robertsons' place. We spread it at the edge of the grasshopper cloud and lit it up. We spent hours running along the fire line to ensure it didn't spread any more than possible and directing the fire into the grasshoppers. It was hard to keep the fire under control, but it worked. By nightfall the insect plague was under control. The south acreage of Mr. Robertson's ranch was a mass of burned grasshoppers and a bleak landscape of plant life eaten down to the roots. There was no chance of anything growing in those fields this season. We knew the grasshoppers weren't gone for good, but it was one temporary victory over the invading hoard.

The insects and weather were accepted obstacles to settling on the prairie and were always a challenge to our little community. But another obstacle, and for many the worst, to homesteading on the plains was the isolation. The vastness of the prairie, the never-ending winds, and the distances made you feel small and insignificant. If neighbors and friends did not help each other the solitude and loneliness would weaken even the strongest mind.

Luckily, I had wonderful friends and neighbors. Our little community of Cherry Ridge loved each other and provided wonderful support and companionship. My initial fears of staying alone and walking alone at night were overcome with the help of my friends. I rarely had an evening without company at my cabin, or my going to visit others. My diary was full of entries about our community. "Alma came over at dinner and stayed all night," and "... walked to Crofts and staid [sic] for dinner." Work teams and drifters would often come through, probably due to my location next to the reservoir. One entry describes how "Frenchy the sheep man wanted to cross our land and we tried to bargain for a few lambs." Another explains how "a couple of 'tumble-weeds' came through and wanted some dinner." We obliged. Leo was a constant companion, visiting almost every day during the summer. The Furchtbars – who had a larger house – frequently hosted dinner gatherings, and my house was the location of music and singing, since I had the only phonograph and piano in the area. Although the prairie could get lonely, we never really felt that way. It was too much fun.

The spring of 1915 was followed by another hot, dry summer. We soon became aware of the importance of our reservoir. After being in town for a weekend Father and I returned to the shack to discover my neighbor to the west, Mr. Harbolt, had diverted water from the reservoir. The pond was low and we had little left for irrigation. Father was furious and threatened to take his gun and go after Mr. Harbolt, whose family owned the bank in Chinook.

"That bastard," shouted Father. "His daddy owns the bank so he thinks he can get away with anything. Well those connections don't give him any protection out here. Let me go find him. He thinks he so special that he can steal our water. Well, it ain't going to happen."

I was able to keep Father from going after Mr. Harbolt, but the potential damage was significant. The pond was designed to irrigate the acreage we had claimed under the Desert Land Act, which specified the land had to be irrigated every year before you could prove up a claim. If Mr. Harbolt diverted enough to keep us from irrigating, we could lose our land.

The next day Father, Leo, and a hired hand irrigated the land all day with what little water was left in the reservoir. Then they rebuilt the canal so it was entirely on our land. Mr. Harbolt was nowhere to be seen, which pleased Father. He was sure Mr. Harbolt would try to sneak over at night and divert the water, so for the next few nights we all slept at the edge of the pond. After three nights we decided he had learned his lesson, but we continued to watch for intruders at the reservoir.

A few days after we returned to sleeping at home, we saw a light at the reservoir late at night. Leo grabbed his gun and investigated for two hours, but did not find anyone or any damage. He came back to my shack, but sat outside all night watching for unusual activity at the pond. Mr. Harbolt did things his own way. He never did anything illegal, just annoying. Our little community learned to be aware of his tricks and keep everyone informed.

The natives were also an interesting source of company, laughter, and mischief. Their children were adorable and always smiling. They reminded me of the natives I frequently saw growing up in Melrose. Mother always cared for and fed the native children around Melrose, so I continued her loving care of the children. I always had a bit of food for them and often some hard candy, which was their favorite. They loved having their picture taken. I had bought a small Kodak Brownie camera during my winter stay in Havre. Once the children discovered I had a camera they would visit and sit until I took their picture. Then they would impatiently wait for me to get it developed, coming back every week until the photos returned from Havre.

Their parents, on the other hand, seemed shiftless, lazy, and full of mischief. You could never trust them. When I fed the children I always had to watch the adults because they would walk into the house and steal anything they could. To them it wasn't a crime – just a game to see if they could get away with it. For me, it meant constantly being vigilant when they were around.

The war in Europe was the news of the year. Every newspaper was filled with stories of the ghastly killing along the frontlines in France. The war had evolved into a stalemate of trench warfare and neither side could gain any ground on the other. Terrible deaths were reported as each side attempted to move the others out of their trenches. The Germans used poison gas and then declared unrestricted submarine warfare.

The submarine warfare was especially serious for the United States since we were trying to keep the ocean open for free trade. President Wilson continued to try to convince the world the United States was a neutral nation, but it became harder and harder to support the position. My German friends were convinced the English and French were the evil side of the war and were committing the worst atrocities, while Leo's French relatives wrote about how terrible the Germans were. Of course being so close to the border, we met many Canadians who were critical of our neutrality and couldn't understand why we wouldn't give more support to the British.

Then in early May 1915 news arrived in Chinook that changed our minds about the war. A German submarine sank the *RMS Lusitania*, killing almost 1,200 passengers, including over 120 Americans. The United States was outraged and suddenly everyone wanted to help the British defeat Germany. President Wilson continued to stress neutrality and after his protests the Germans announced they would stop their unrestricted submarine warfare. It seemed we had avoided the war, at least for a while.

The war was a big benefit for us on the prairie, though. The crop fields in Europe were devastated by the war. Consequently, we were the major source of grain for all of Europe. We were encouraged to grow as much as possible and the price of all grains rose rapidly. If America could stay out of the war it would be very profitable for everyone in the country.

I planted forty acres of flax in addition to my usual acreage of hay and alfalfa for forage. I also cleared, plowed, and harrowed another twenty acres to leave fallow until next year. Red Green planted oats on the twenty acres he rented from me. The weather was hot, but not as dry as last year, and the crops grew well. I was excited about the chance to get in a good harvest and make a small profit.

Summer on the High Plains of Montana could bring a variety of weather as wide as the endless horizons. Days could be calm and pleasant. On those days, I would eat my evening meal in the yard and enjoy the quiet, exquisite beauty of the sunset. Other days could bring relentless heat and drying winds. Those were the days I had to take special care of the livestock and crops to protect them as much as possible. Then there were spectacular thunderstorms. I would watch the clouds build on the western horizon and slowly move across the prairie. With no trees to obscure the view I could see storms twenty or thirty miles away. Often there would be sunshine and intense heat on my homestead but raining twenty miles away on the horizon. When a storm did reach my ranch the thunder and lightning were beyond description. Thunder would roll in a continuous roar across the land and lightning would send brilliant bolts of energy to earth in a magnificent display of nature's power. Our biggest concern was the lightning would start a brushfire, but the beauty of the display made the storms exciting to watch.

The summer of 1915 provided more rain than the previous year and the fields looked better than any year since I had been on the prairie. With grain prices high due to the continuing war it looked to finally be a profitable harvest season.

Again, Red Green and his crew were in high demand during the harvest. His positive attitude and reputation for hard work paid off. Everyone in the Cherry Ridge community hired him to work their fields. He was busy from early morning until late at night. When he worked the fields nearby he brought me chickens or pork to cook for his men in exchange for working my fields. Of course I obliged. They were in our area for almost two weeks during which time I had plenty of fun and laughs feeding his crew and playing music for them. In addition to all the good fun, they harvested 240 bushels of flax for me. When I took it to market I made a nice profit and finally believed I could successfully prove up my claim on the land.

In late October the temperature dropped suddenly to zero degrees and we were hit with an early season snowstorm. It only lasted about twelve hours, but I was isolated in my shack where I fought to stay warm and keep the fire going in my stove. The wind blew through cracks in the walls and the chill came in under the door. I realized I was going to have to do some serious improvements to my home if I ever intended to stay through the winter. But, for this year, I was headed back to Havre for the winter. I took a room at the Montana Hotel. I did not want to stay in Father's small apartment and I also did not plan on being in town as long as previous winters. I enjoyed the prairie and my home too much, even when the weather was rough.

It had been a tumultuous year for Leo and me. We still saw each other as often as possible but we had more than our normal number of arguments, usually over trivial events. Small things challenging his masculinity upset him. Once, he got bucked off his horse into a cactus. I spent over an hour picking quills from his legs and buttocks. I couldn't suppress my laughter each time I thought of how helpless and funny he looked. He didn't see the humor and became more and more angry, finally storming out of the cabin. He wouldn't talk to me for two days. Another time, he didn't like the haircut I gave him. He accused me of making him look silly on purpose and refused to see me for almost a week. We argued over what crops to plant and when to harvest them. And most of all, he seemed to be terribly jealous of my friends.

I hoped being in town for the winter would bring us closer and we would finally come to a decision about marriage. It had become a very sensitive subject. Leo never wanted to talk about it, and it only created stress, so I tried to be very careful about mentioning anything related to marriage.

To complicate things, the Great Northern opened new stations and sent Leo to train the station personnel. He was frequently gone for up to two weeks at a time. While he was away I would continue to go to social events, but was careful to not discuss them when he returned.

In early November, when Leo was out of town on railroad business, the Elks had a masquerade ball. My friends, Lydia and Nell, convinced me to go with them. I thought Leo wouldn't mind if I was with two other women.

When we arrived we discovered Harry Green at the dance. He explained he had come to town to find some winter construction work, but his freshly bathed look and clean clothes indicated he may have been planning on some social life, too. Shortly after he arrived he walked over and started talking to Lydia, Nell, and me. Then, much to my surprise, he asked me to dance. We had a great time, dancing, laughing, and talking. At one point, during a break in the music, he asked, "You and Leo DeLorimier are still a couple, right?"

I was having fun and flirtatiously responded, "Why do you ask Mr. Green? Are you flirting with me?"

Harry blushed, laughed, and said, "Oh, no. Just thought I'd ask. You never can tell, ya' know."

I smiled back and continued flirting. "Well, yes we are still together. But he's not here tonight and I'm having a nice time with you. Are you having fun?"

"Oh yes, I'm having a great time. I always do when I'm with you, Mabel. But I thought I'd ask how you two were getting on. I hope you didn't find it too personal."

"Not at all. It's a fair question. Let's go dance some more," I said as I pulled him back out on the dance floor.

On the way home Lydia and Nell teased me about Harry.

"You spent the whole night with him. Was he making sweet on you or something?" Nell asked.

Lydia added with a laugh, "Oh, I saw Mabel making sweet on him. I think she's got a crush on him."

"He is a sweet guy," said Nell. "If he wasn't so set on Mabel, I'd go after him myself. I think he's much cuter than Mr. DeLorimier, Mabel. I think you should change beaus." Lydia and Nell both laughed out loud.

"Stop it," I said. "Yes, I had a good time with Harry, but he's just a good friend. He's very helpful at the ranch, but don't get any ideas. Leo is my man and I'm not chasing anyone else. Now don't say anything to Leo. He can be jealous of my having a good time when he's not around."

But there were no secrets in Havre so he found out soon enough. When he heard I had gone to the dance he was furious.

"How can you go to a dance without me?" he roared jealously. "If I'm your beau you should not be dancing with other men and gallivanting around like a loose woman. It's embarrassing for me."

I found his attitude unacceptable. "I don't like your domineering attitude. When you are here I will do everything with you – I love you. But when you are gone, I'm going to do things on my own. I will continue to go out with my friends. I love music and dancing. I love to go to social events. I'm not going to sit here and do nothing while you're gone. Don't you trust me? Don't you believe I can go out and have a good time and still be loyal and love you?"

He looked at me with a strange look. "Maybe you are too independent for me. Maybe I want a wife who will listen to her husband and stay home for him. I don't enjoy hearing of your activities while I'm gone. Yes, I am jealous. I don't like other men dancing with you and I don't want people around town talking about you and me."

We had had this discussion before and it always ended badly. But I was angry and wasn't going to let him get the last word. "Who do you think I am? You sometimes treat me like a possession – like I'm fun to have around, but not someone you want to spend the rest of your life with. What is it? Do you think I'm your possession? Why shouldn't I be able to do things on my own? Why can't I walk downtown by myself? Why can't I go to a dance or a play without you? You can't always be there. Why can't I make my own decisions? I don't think you trust me."

We were both angry and yelling. Leo was at a loss for words and turned to leave. "Well, maybe after all this time we need to understand we aren't made for each other. Good-bye."

He was gone. We had had many fights, but this seemed to be the worst. I wasn't going to be bossed around by him and be the submissive woman he wanted, but, for some unknown reason, I still loved him. I didn't want to let him go and thought maybe I could come around to his way of thinking. Maybe we could come to some sort of compromise on all this.

Two days passed and I didn't hear anything from him. I had calmed down, but knew it would take him longer to come around. I knew Leo would not come to me, so I gave in and went to his house. I knocked on his door and apologized right away. He also apologized and suddenly we were in each other's arms kissing and hugging. We laughed at ourselves and promised to listen to the needs of the other.

That night we made love for the first time since my miscarriage. It was wonderful. I believed Leo and I were finally going to get it right.

The next day I wrote in my dairy, "Love is bigger than pride and if it isn't, well, it's not the right kind. And I thank heaven ours is. No matter how ravingly [sic] angry we are, when it's all over we are just that much sweeter."

The rest of the winter went by quickly. Leo and I went to a dance, movie, or party every weekend. Everyone in Havre knew we were a couple, yet he still made no attempts to ask me to marry him and generally refused to talk about it. We slept together and had relations more often. I overcame my earlier prudish hesitations and believed it would finally end in marriage for Leo and me, especially if I became pregnant again.

The new year brought new problems though. The Great Northern wanted Leo to work at a new station in eastern Montana. The Lambert, Montana station had only been open for a few months. It was having problems and needed a new dispatcher.

"I won't be gone long," he promised. "I will get them in shape, then come back. It's too cold to work at the ranch anyways."

"I'm not worried about the ranch. I'm worried about you leaving. Can we talk about getting married when you return?"

"Mabel – You know I am hesitant to discuss marriage, but I promise we will talk about it when I get back."

He left at the end of January, promising to return within a month.

In late February Father helped me move back to the homestead before he left for a railroad construction job in eastern Washington State. I was alone again, but was becoming used to it and wasn't as afraid as I had been in the past. I settled into my daily routine of milking the cow, feeding the horses, caring for the early crops, and preparing for the summer.

Then the morning sickness started and I missed my monthly. I was pregnant again. This time I knew the symptoms and wasn't surprised. Leo and I had been together many times in the last couple of months. I actually hoped to get pregnant before he left for Lambert because I was sure it would convince him to finally marry me. But he left before we knew I was pregnant. I decided not to tell him in a letter. He had said he would only be gone a month – I would wait until he returned.

I wrote him almost every day, but received nothing in return. In my letters I begged and pleaded for him to respond and at least tell me he was safe. Finally, after he had been gone for over a month, I got a short letter. It didn't say much. He was very busy, didn't have time to write letters, and, worst of all, was not returning to Havre until June, at the earliest. He said nothing about missing me, or loving me. He didn't even sign it "with love."

I cried for two days. I was pregnant again and Leo didn't know. I was starting to show so decided I had to tell him. I wrote him a straightforward letter explaining I was pregnant and probably due in August. It was, without question, his child.

I did not get a response.

As before, Alma and Bessie were wonderful. They visited every day and kept my spirits up. Bessie, especially, became my most trusted friend. She had just delivered her third child, Lester, so she understood what I was going through better than anyone. She guided me through the morning sickness, my food cravings, and helped me with work around the ranch. The spring chores were a great distraction from the depressing thoughts of Leo's absence and my pregnancy. I decided not to go into town until I heard something from Leo. I did not want to face any of his family or friends without an answer to the obvious question about our baby.

The spring thaw made the prairie a mess of mud and slop. One cold, windy morning, when I was feeling especially depressed over my situation, Red Green stopped by.

"Good morning Miss Richmond," he politely said, although I had told him a hundred times to call me Mabel. "I noticed you haven't done much with your fields this spring and was wondering if you needed some help? I'd be glad to do some work around here for you. Maybe I could help you plant a bit more and we could split the crop so it won't cost you anything."

I was now over three months pregnant and starting to show. I hadn't been to town and only a few people knew. I wasn't feeling well and really didn't want to talk to anyone, but Red was smiling his enchanting smile and being especially polite. I couldn't be cross with him. "Thank you Red. I appreciate your offer. You're right. I haven't done much this spring. I guess I've been a little lazy."

Red looked at me with a quizzical look on his face. "It's probably not proper to ask, but I have often been accused of being too direct. I have to ask – are you pregnant?"

I couldn't help myself. I was so upset and embarrassed I started to cry. "Yes," was all I could say.

"I'm so sorry to upset you. I wanted to say congratulations. I didn't expect your reaction. I assume Leo is the father? But he hasn't been at his cabin and I haven't seen him all spring. Is everything okay?" He was trying to be kind and understanding, not knowing what was going on.

"Oh, Red. I don't want to be a burden to you and I'm so sorry to cry. You caught me on a bad day. Would you like to come in and have a cup of tea? If you don't mind it would be good to talk to someone."

Red looked upset but relieved to be able to discuss things. "Yes, I'd like to talk. Thank you."

We talked most of the morning. I told him everything about Leo and me. He listened intently and seemed concerned. We had tea and some two-day-old stale cookies. He said he loved my cooking and my music. I told him I loved his singing. Finally, he got me laughing about something and by the time he left I felt much better and knew he was a true friend.

I told Father when he returned from his winter trip to Seattle. As expected he was furious, first at me for being – in his words, "so stupid!" – then at Leo for not writing. For two days he was unapproachable, but then he finally settled down.

"I believe Leo will return," he said. "You have told him you are pregnant, and he's an honorable man. He'll be back, just give him some time." I never knew if Father truly believed that, or said it to ease my concerns.

Red brought his crew over and worked twice as much land as was cleared the previous year. He cleared another forty acres to lay fallow, planted twenty acres of oats, twenty of barley, and another twenty for hay and alfalfa. The war was still going on and grain prices were high, so it was smart to plant as much as possible. I agreed to split the crop with him, since he and his men were doing all the work. It was really the only way to get anything done, since I refused to do any heavy labor and risk losing a baby again.

I still had not heard anything from Leo. I tried to give him the benefit of the doubt, but I was getting angry and frustrated. Why couldn't he at least send a short note? What was he doing? Was he abandoning me again because of the pregnancy? I didn't have a clue and no one could help. Bessie, Alma, and even Red tried to cheer me up and keep me from thinking about Leo, but my ever-growing belly would not allow me to forget my situation.

Then one day in early May, Father came from town and delivered a letter Leo had written two weeks before. I ran into my cabin for some privacy and ripped it open.

> *My dearest Mabel,*
>
> *I am writing this to tell you I am fine and now living in Lambert full time. The Great North-*

ern has offered me a promotion to regional station chief. It is more money and more responsibility and I love the job. As you know, I've always been partial to working and living in the city. That has always been one of our biggest disagreements. I'm comfortable here and don't anticipate returning to Havre or the ranch anytime soon.

I have to tell you something I know is going to hurt you, but we've always said we had to be honest with each other, so here it is. I have met someone here and started a new life. She is a good Catholic woman and I think we are truly in love. I know you and I have been a couple for over five years, but I've felt a serious strain on our relationship lately. I didn't know how to tell you while I was there. I had to get away before I was sure I was not in love with you.

I'm very sorry to hurt you. You are a wonderful woman, strong and intelligent, and I know you will be fine. Please understand how special our time together was, but also that I have to live my life and do what's best for me. Good luck.

With love and respect,

Leo

I read the letter over and over. I was devastated. He never acknowledged my pregnancy. He didn't mention my having his baby. I could not believe he was so coldhearted. I cried, I screamed, and I wanted to go to Lambert and confront him. But I couldn't. I was stuck here in my little shack in the middle of the Great Plains, alone, and miles from anywhere. I was twenty-six, unmarried, and with child. I didn't know what to do. I was lost.

Moving On

"Didn't you tell me your mother always said to move on and take each new day as a challenge?" Bessie was trying to cheer me up after reading Leo's letter. "What was it she said about life being like a book?"

I looked up at her. "Life is a collection of different chapters, and when you get to the end of one chapter you have to turn the page and keep going without looking back."

"So, you've come to the end of a chapter in your life. Don't look back. Move on." She was being very persuasive. "You can do it. You have always prided yourself on being strong and independent. You won't be the first woman to have a baby out of wedlock and you won't be the last. The secret of success is how you handle adversity. I want you to be happy for the child you are carrying. I know you will be a wonderful, caring, loving mother. So get up and get going."

I loved her for being so positive, but I still missed Leo and couldn't believe he had abandoned me. I was totally shocked by his letter and could not think of anything in the last year that might have led to his decision. I was more upset about losing him than I was about being pregnant. When I said something about it to Bessie she told me, "Let him go. Leo obviously was not right for you. It took a long time to see it, but the two of you were not meant for each other. Let him go."

Red Green was working in our neighborhood more this summer than in the past. He always came and worked my fields two or three days a week. When he wasn't in my fields he was helping the Crofts or the Slonakers. I'm not sure if there was more work in the area or if he was coming by to visit, but I saw him almost every day. In a different situation – if I was not pregnant and still pining for Leo – I might think he was courting me. But it didn't even cross my mind.

The more I saw him, the more I respected him. He was good looking – a bit over six feet tall, slender, and strong – and of course his wavy red hair always made him stand out in a crowd. He was outgoing, talked loud and fast, and was happy to be the center of attention. But he was also personable and sensitive. He always had a funny story and wasn't afraid to make himself the butt of a good joke. He would do anything to help a friend. I appreciated his can-do spirit. It seemed there was never a job he couldn't handle and he was willing to work long hard hours to get the job done.

Often he would stop and talk. If he had his crew with him he would stay for only a few minutes, but when he was working my land he was usually alone. On those days I would make supper for both of us and he would stay into the evening eating and talking. Often he would sleep in the barn because it was too late for him to go back to his cabin. It didn't bother him to sleep with the horses and I enjoyed his company.

We talked about everything – our families, our backgrounds, and our dreams. He was only two years older than me – born in 1888 in Jackson County, Michigan where his family still lived. He was the second of seven children with one older and two younger brothers, and three sisters.

"I'm a third generation Irish Catholic," he would say. "My grandparents came over in the middle 1800s. Mother's maiden name was Riley and she is very traditional. Me – I don't care much about that stuff, but it's important to her. Guess I'm the black sheep in the family." He let out a big belly laugh as if he was proud to be the family rebel.

"You know, I even changed my name out here. It made my father mad, but it's really a simple thing."

"Why did you change your name?" I asked.

"There is another Harry Green in the area. He lives in Big Sandy and we kept getting each other's mail. So I started putting an "e" on the end on my name. Now I spell it G-R-E-E-N-E. I have fun with it and answer to either spelling. It's not a problem around here, although I sometimes forget which spelling to use on things I have to sign. I try to make sure I use it on mail though. That way the postman knows which Harry Green to deliver to."

I chuckled. "Seems a little unnecessary to me, but if it works, I guess it's okay."

"I like a little joke now and then," he said with a mischievous grin. "It keeps people guessing. I have even invented a new middle name sometimes. Sometimes, I'll sign papers 'Harry Harrison Greene' instead of 'Harry E. Green' just to see if anyone notices."

By now I was laughing hard. "Now that seems especially silly. Does anyone really care?"

"Don't seem to. No one has ever said anything, and I just keep chuckling to myself."

He was always vague about how he ended up in Montana, simply saying he left Michigan in 1912 and worked his way west until he came to Havre to claim his homestead in

1913. I got the feeling he wanted to get out from under his mother's domination but he had a better story.

"There's a story goin' around I left home in a hurry after punching a guy out at a dance one night in Michigan. Thought he was dead so my buddy and I hit the road before anyone could catch us. He wasn't dead, but by then we were on the road. Worked in Ohio, Canada, and lots of other places before coming to Montana."

"So, is it true? Is that why you came west?" I didn't think he was the type to hit someone.

"Well – I'm not saying it is, or isn't, but it's a good story and I'll leave it at that. As I said, I like to be a little mysterious." Then he quickly changed the subject.

I didn't really care about his past. He never displayed a temper when he was with me. He was always so sincere and honest. And it was nice to have a man to talk to.

"I love it out here on the plains," Red said often. "There is so much freedom. There is plenty of work, I can set my own schedule, and do what I want to do. And everyone out here is in the same situation. There aren't any rich or poor – we're all just working to survive and get ahead a little bit."

"Yes, very true," I said. "But what do you want down the line? What do you want four or five years from now?"

Harry had the answer right away, as if he'd been thinking about it a lot. "I'd love to get more land and be a successful farmer and rancher. I think there is plenty of opportunity out here. With grain prices high and trade good I ought to be able to make some money. There is still plenty of land to be had. I would like to settle down, have a wife and big family, and a successful ranch."

"Sounds nice. I like it out here, too. But I'm torn. I enjoy social, urban things, but not as much as I used to. Out

159

here on the prairie those things don't matter. I want to be the woman my mother raised me to be, but I also love it out here where I can relax, not worry about clothes, my hair, or social obligations. I like the hard work and excitement here on the ranch, but I'm going to have a baby and being an unwed mother, alone and far from any help, may not be the best option. When I think of it, I get scared and depressed. Maybe I should move back to town where there is more help."

He gave me a look of great care and concern. "Are you convinced Leo isn't coming back? You still haven't heard anything?"

I shook my head. "I haven't heard anything since the last letter. I wrote him again and begged him to recognize the baby and come back, but he hasn't written anything. It's been over a month and I am sure he got the letter. I still can't believe he could be so callous, but I'm starting to accept the reality of it and admit he probably is not going to come back." I sniffed back some tears and looked up at Harry for sympathy.

He reached across the table and held my hand. "I'm so sorry. I shouldn't have brought it up. You'll be okay Mabel – you have great friends and a wonderful community here to support you. But I also have something else to say. You always talk about what your mother would say or think. I know you love and respect the memory of your mother and you want to be the woman she raised you to be. I understand all that. But from what you've told me about Mary Isabell Richmond, I don't think she raised you to be a quiet, subservient little woman to some dominating man who makes all the decisions. She wanted you to be a lady, but – and you've said this many times yourself – a courageous, self-sufficient woman who makes her own decisions and lives her own life. I think you've forgotten who you are. I think you need to start living your life, your way. You can honor your mother by being yourself."

I thought for a minute then said, "You're right. One of her favorite sayings was 'Be yourself.' Thank you for reminding me." I didn't pull my hand back but let it linger in his for a while. I smiled at him and he smiled back then got up to go.

"I'm sorry to be blunt and direct, but I think you've been wallowing in your predicament long enough. Time for you to get up and accept where you are and who you are. Now, I've got to get going. I'll see you in a couple of days," he said.

"I look forward to it. Thank you. Good night," was all I said. But after he was gone I thought about what he had said. Harry was right – I was trying to live a life filled with illusions of what I thought Mother wanted. I overlooked the toughness Mother had displayed in her own life living on the edge of civilization, moving around, and raising me mostly on her own. I had forgotten how the honest, practical, and sensible side of her found the positive in every situation. I'd forgotten how she could stand up to Father and challenge him. I had focused too much on the fancy hairdos, lace dresses, and socially acceptable language and missed the intelligence, foresight, and vision my mother always displayed. Those were the attributes I wanted to emulate. Suddenly, being pregnant and alone on the prairie seemed to be a challenge – the type of challenge Mother would accept and ultimately embrace. I could do the same.

The next day Father came out to the ranch to visit. He had been in Idaho for a construction job for the last two weeks.

"Papa, what do you think of Harry Green?" I asked over supper.

"Red? Good man. Hardworking, honest, and funny. A bit of a big head, but not in a bad way. He's done a lot of good work around these parts. He has a good reputation for putting in an honest day's work in the fields. And he has a good crew, too. It takes a good man to keep field hands working hard. Good hunter, too, I've heard." He gave me a quizzical look. "Why do you ask? You haven't taken a fancy to him, have you?"

"No – how can I? I'm carrying another man's child. I'm sure no man would be interested in me right now. I was just asking. He works our fields every week and often stays around to eat. He seems sincere and kind, like a gentle giant."

Papa laughed. "You like him then. I can tell. If you're cooking for him, you must like him."

I was a bit surprised by Father's statement but realized there was some truth to what he said. "I suppose so. He's very nice – and handsome, too." I was embarrassed to say it and felt the blood rushing to my cheeks. "I can't believe he isn't dating other women around here."

Papa laughed. "You keep feeding him those good meals and he won't have the time or desire to look at other women."

Two days later, while Father was still at the ranch, Harry showed up and invited him to go hunting. He told Father he had a secret spot to share with him, so the two of them rode off on their horses. Two days later they returned talking and laughing about their trip, even though they only had one deer to show for their time together. Father took the kill to the barn to clean and butcher. Harry stayed at the cabin and said he wanted to talk.

At first he talked about hunting with Papa and how much fun they had. Apparently, they had bonded and discovered they had many things in common. Then he suddenly seemed to hesitate and be at a loss for words. He stopped talking.

"What is it, Harry?" I asked. "It's not like you to be quiet."

"Will you marry me?" he suddenly blurted out. "I asked your father on the trip. That's why I wanted to go hunting with him – to get his permission."

I was caught totally off guard and surprised. "What? Is this one of your jokes? I'm pregnant with another man's child. Why would you want to marry me?"

"I don't care about who the father is, I will love the child as if it were my own. And, besides, if we are married, it will be my child. I've loved you for a long time Mabel, but I didn't think I had a chance with Leo around. But he's gone and apparently not coming back. I'm here, and not going anywhere. There is no one else I want to be with. My mother will be furious I'm not marrying a Catholic, but I don't care. I'm sick of all her Catholic preaching anyways. She's not here to see how wonderful you are. What do you say – will you?"

"Yes," was all I could say. I couldn't believe it came out so easily. He stepped closer and gave me a big hug and we held each other for a long time. I realized I had stronger feelings for Harry than I wanted to admit. I still had feelings for Leo – he was a good man and we had some good times together, but I never felt as comfortable and happy as I did with Harry. I hadn't let my heart get involved with Harry, but suddenly everything seemed to fall into place.

In the evening I pulled out the letters Leo had written. I hadn't noticed how few there were. I had written him ten letters to every one I received. As I reread them, I noticed most of his letters had few expressions of love or affection. I reflected on our five years together and realized our relationship had been very one-sided. I couldn't believe how naïve I had been. I had been the romantic one. I was the one expressing love and devotion. Leo had enjoyed my company and having someone in town to be his partner at social events. He even enjoyed me in his bed, but he had never truly expressed his love. I thought of our frequent arguments. I always thought they weren't very serious and led to good reunions. But now I realized how they were indicative of our considerable differences. I was actively pursuing him and loving him, but he didn't share my feelings.

I even started wondering if he had been stringing me along for all those years. Had there been other women in the railroad towns he had to visit? Did he have a secret girlfriend in town? Had I been one of a number of lovesick girls along the Hi-Line he had been visiting? The more I thought about it, the crazier my ideas got. Though I had no proof, I couldn't help wondering if I was one of many girls in Leo's life.

I was determined to start anew. I burned the letters. It was the past and I wasn't going back.

A Prairie Child: 1916

Harry worked hard during the summer. Grain prices were high and there was plenty of opportunity for Red and his crew to help the settlers in the Cherry Ridge area. He was still living in his cabin about eight miles away. The Homestead Act was complicated about ownership when two homesteaders married, especially in regard to the woman's claim. Besides, Harry still had all his livestock – mostly horses he was breaking – and equipment on his land. He did not want to move until his claim was proved up. Harry was in the last year of his three-year requirement and didn't want any problems with his proof. He had applied for final proof the previous fall and had to stay on the land until he received official approval. His patent – the official recognition of ownership from the Department of Interior – was approved and he got the deed in May of 1916.

We decided my land would be the center of our holdings since I had more acreage and the reservoir. He came over as often as possible, usually five or six times a week. Sometimes his visits were only for an hour or two depending on where he was working. But if he was in the area he would stay for supper and spend the night. Whenever he was there the mood was happy, full of fun, laughs, and pleasant conversation. We never argued.

I was busy around the house with the domestic chores and preparing for the baby, but it was obvious we were going to need a bigger place once Harry moved in. Right after Harry and I became engaged, Father began building an addition to my house. He built a twelve-by-sixteen-foot living room and an eight-by-sixteen-foot screened porch. When the construction was completed the house had three large rooms – a kitchen, bedroom and living room – with a large, covered porch and an underground food cellar. It was some house for a dry-lander. I could even move my piano into a larger area in the living room.

Harry also wanted to improve our land, making it a full-scale ranch with more livestock, grain, and outbuildings. He and Father enlarged the barn, built another shed for horses, and enlarged the corral area, because we planned on buying more cattle and horses. The cattle would fatten up on our pasture land and he would break the horses and sell them at auction for both farming and riding. He also introduced me to his brand – the Z/T.

I was curious. "Is there a particular reason your brand is Z/T?" I asked.

Harry chuckled his mischievous laugh. "Nope. I've had it since 1914. Had to go all the way over to Dodson to get it registered. It's simple to make and I liked the way it looked. I can just use a straight piece of hot iron to put the brand on. I don't have to have some fancy blacksmith work of art. But if anyone else asks, I might make up a little story, just to keep some mystery to it." Then he laughed some more.

I looked at him and smiled. "I guess it doesn't matter, I'm just happy to be part of the Z/T Ranch."

Harry wrote home often, especially to his youngest sister, Hazel. She was the most sympathetic ear back in Michigan. She, in turn, kept him informed of events and family discussions. He wrote his mother and father after we became engaged. His mother was furious he was not marrying a Catholic girl and refused to answer any of his letters. She even told other members of the family not to reply to Harry's letters. Consequently, the letters to Hazel became an even more important line of communication.

In May, right after Harry proposed and I accepted, he shared his letter to Hazel with me.

> *I am engaged to a girl here by the name of Mabel Richmond. She has a homestead not far from me and a sweet girl too I think... Sis I've got it bad. I think there is nobody quite so nice as she is. Would you like to write her? I told Mother about her and she don't like it a bit because she is not a Catholic...*

Harry suggested I add a postscript to his letter to introduce myself – at least to Hazel and hopefully, indirectly to the rest of the family. I wanted to let them know how much I loved Harry and ensure them our relationship wasn't just a case of prairie isolation convenience.

> *Dear Hazel:*
> *I've meant to write and get acquainted, tho I feel I know you very well indeed from hearing so much about you from Red...*
> *Hazel, you don't know what a wonderful brother you have or you would be out here on the first*

train. He is oh, so thoughtful always. We so often wish you would come out here and I'm sure you would like it. My land is about six or eight miles from his but he is putting in the Richmond crop this year and you may be sure, I'm going to keep him as long as I can. I have a neighbor girl working for me and "chaperoning" us.

The Bear Paw Mountains are really about fifty miles from here but look about ten and we often go fishing there for mountain trout. You see, Hazel, I'm trying to make you want to come out and when you do, you are to stay here. Why don't you come out and teach? There is a school only about three miles from Red's you could get and they pay $65.00/mo. Wages are good all over Montana. I would like to teach myself but father and I are absolutely alone in the world and he throws a fit every time I suggest it. He thinks I do my share by holding down the claim for seven months out of the year only that is a picnic for me.

Red is waiting for me to play for him and has just said "For Heaven's sake, is that all to Hazel." so maybe I had better stop.

Sincerely

Mabel Richmond

Harry did not mention I was pregnant. He figured it would be better to address it later. Knowing his mother would be angry, he figured he was better off crossing one bridge at a time. I agreed.

We agreed to marry right after the baby was born. By then he would have the final proof on his land and I would have a good year towards my proving up. It would be much easier to work around the homestead laws if we waited. Besides, he was busy from dawn to dusk and said it didn't matter when we got married. Father, on the other hand, was concerned. He was always aware of how things would affect his reputation. He didn't want the people in Havre or Chinook to know his daughter had a child out of wedlock. I had not been to either city since I started showing, so only the neighbors on the prairie were aware of my condition. Father wanted to make it appear Harry and I had been married before I became pregnant. He was obsessed with the entire situation.

Bessie visited every day and checked on my condition as my due date got closer. She helped me deal with the emotional ups and downs of pregnancy and told me what to expect from day to day. She usually brought her youngest child over and I learned how to care for a baby from her. She would stay most of the day and keep me company as the two of us did easy chores around the house. I tried to stay active but I would never have been able to get any crop in if it hadn't been for Red and my neighbors helping out. Without a crop I wouldn't be able to prove up my claim.

It was late August and we knew I would deliver soon. On August twenty-sixth Harry went to Canada for a couple days to purchase seed for the winter wheat. Canada was closer than Havre and the seed was cheaper, so it was his usual source. He kissed me good-bye, said he would be back as soon as he could, and made me promise to not have the baby while he was gone. I told him I would try.

My labor pains started two days later, the morning of August 28, 1916. We had hired a young girl to help me for the last two months of my pregnancy. When she came in for the day my contractions were already four minutes apart and the pain was intense.

"Oh – I don't think this little one is going to wait much longer," I panted between the contractions. "Phoebe, run over to Slonaker's and get Bessie. She can help. Please hurry."

I was alone and in labor. I wasn't sure what to do. I wished Harry could be there, but it was not going to be. I tried to stay calm, but the contractions seized my body. I had never experienced such intense pain. I screamed and cried with each contraction and tried not to push, but suddenly I felt the baby slipping from my body. I reached between my legs and pulled the small baby girl to my stomach. She gave a strong, loud cry and I knew everything would be all right. I wasn't sure what to do next so I lay quiet with my dear little one marveling at this new life I had brought into the world. When Bessie arrived about twenty minutes later I was lying in bed peacefully with my beautiful baby girl.

"So Mabel, you couldn't wait for me could you? Had to do it all by yourself. How appropriate. A girl. I'll bet you will raise her to be just like you. Stubborn, opinionated, and confident." She laughed. "Okay – I've got some work to do here. You relax, the hard part is over." Bessie quickly got some clean towels and hot water. She cut the cord, cleaned the baby and me, and got me a cup of tea. She was wonderful.

"Oh, thank you for being here. I don't know what I would do without you."

"You did it all by yourself, Mabel." She teased me a bit to release the tension. "Just like always – you had to do it yourself. Congratulations. You are the mother of a lovely little lady. Do you have a name?"

"Yes – I'm going to name her Harriet Isabell after my Aunt Harriet and my mother. Papa will be very happy."

Harry returned from Canada late in the evening. As usual, he called to me from the stable as he was tying up his horse. When I didn't respond right away he figured something was up and hurried into the house.

"Mabel, is everything okay?" was the first thing he said when he saw me in bed.

I looked up and smiled. "Everything is wonderful. I would like to introduce you to Miss Harriet Isabell Richmond."

"Soon to be Harriet Isabell Greene," he quickly responded. He took the baby in his big strong hands and held her gently. "She's so small," was all he said, then put a gentle kiss on her forehead. "I am a happy and proud papa." He slept on the floor next to my bed and woke regularly to look at the baby. I loved the way he accepted me and our little Harriet.

Father drove out to the ranch the next morning. When he arrived he was surprised by all the commotion around the cabin, since everyone in the Cherry Ridge community knew of the birth and had come to see the baby. He came in the house with a roar of laughter and excitement.

"Congratulations Mabel. You make me proud to be your father." He always seemed to think of himself first. "Did I hear the baby's name is Harriet Isabell? Wonderful choice. Your mother would be so touched. Let me see my granddaughter." He swiftly, and gently, swept up Harriet and held her over his head. "Okay little girl. In no time I'm going to teach you to ride and shoot and hunt and fish."

Harry laughed then said, "Wait – don't I get to do that? I am her papa you know."

Father looked over at Harry and laughed in return. "Of course you are. We'll teach her together. Say, don't you two have some unfinished business to attend to?"

"Are you referring to our getting married?" asked Harry. "We were waiting for you to get here. Take your old Model T and get the Justice of the Peace. We can get married right here today if you can find him."

"I'll be back in a couple hours. You better not change your minds while I'm gone." He laughed as he headed towards the door.

I looked at Harry and then shouted to Papa, "Hurry back – we won't be changing our minds. I'm convinced more than ever, I want to marry this man."

On August 29, 1916, Harry E. Greene and I were married in front of my home in the middle of the Montana prairie in the presence of my father, our baby daughter, and our neighbors. It was a simple ceremony and I was exhausted from the events of the last twenty-four hours, but, oh, so happy. The neighbors brought food and we ate well into the night. A bottle of whiskey appeared and we all had a celebratory drink.

As the party went on into the night I quietly excused myself and went inside. I looked at Harriet sleeping soundly in her little crib and reflected on the chain of events that had brought me to this place in my life. I fell asleep with a big smile on my face. Life was good.

Looking Back/Looking Ahead

Harry moved in right after our marriage. His moving in did not change my housework much since he had very few possessions to bring over. It did take a little longer on wash-day to get everything cleaned and dried. We had a simple crib for the baby, but otherwise the addition of two more bodies didn't change much in my cabin. We were determined to stay the winter on the ranch, so Papa had winterized the house when he made the expansions. Everything was very comfortable and cozy.

One day, a couple weeks after the wedding, Father drove out to the ranch and jumped out of his car very excited.

"I got everything taken care of," he said as he hurried over to where I was rocking and feeding Harriet. "I've fixed it so the baby is legitimate and you and Harry got married properly."

"What do you mean, married properly?" I asked, looking up with a bit of a scowl. "I don't like the sound of this."

He explained. "I was concerned the baby was born before your marriage and sooner or later people would start talking and wonder about the timing. Someday Leo might come back and say the baby was his. I knew you didn't want that to happen, so I fixed it."

"Papa – What did you do? Red and I have been legally married and nobody is going to take our baby."

"Right, I couldn't agree more, but you know how some people are. So, I got you a new marriage certificate. It says you were married December seventh of last year. It was easy since I've known Pastor Christler at St. Mark's Episcopal Church for years. He agreed to sign a backdated certificate of marriage. Now you can say you were married and the child was legitimate."

I looked at Father and frowned. "What did you have to pay? I'm guessing the pastor didn't do it for free."

"Yes, I had to make a significant contribution to the church, but it's between the pastor and me. You don't need to worry about it. Come on, accept it and allow me this bit of skullduggery." Father had a very satisfied look on his face and I knew there would be no talking him out of it.

When Harry came home Father explained it all to him. We looked at the "Certificate of Marriage" from the church and realized it was probably as official as anything we would get.

Harry roared with laughter. "Why didn't I think of this? It's the sort of trick I usually come up with. Good thinking Ed! Mabel, I guess we've been married nine months and didn't know it. I should have moved in long ago. We will have to celebrate our anniversary in December. Maybe my mother will be happier when she finds out we were married in December. As long as we are together, I could care less."

Soon after Harry wrote to sister Hazel, since his mother still wasn't writing to him. We included a snapshot to give everyone an idea of what the two of us looked like together.

... I have writen [sic] home three times and received no ans. not to one of my letters. Well Sister I've kept a lot from the folks. Maybe I haven't done right by doing so but you know how mother is... But I'm going to tell you now and don't want you to tell, I am married - have been ever cince [sic] Dec. 7, 1915. And that is not all. We have a little daughter. Her name is Harriet she is some girl and some red hair...

... I did expect to go home but it don't look like they wanted to see me so have given it up. Maybe they will be glad to see me some day.

Must close with best regards from your loving Bro.
Red
(Mabel will write you a few lines)

**

My Dear Hazel -
Doubtless you've read Harry's letter first and I know how surprised you'll be. Know we should have told you sooner but, besides my father, very few people knew it. Red had to stay on his homestead last winter and it was too cold for me in his house so he came to town as often as he could in the three months I was in. Baby was rather a

surprise party for us too - we didn't look for her for some little time - I planned to be in town - but I over did and the young lady and her mother were all alone. I had a girl working for me but she had gone to get someone so I was here alone. But oh, the Baby is so sweet and Red is the dearest Man in the world. He has always been wonderful to me but even more so, if possible since baby came.

Hazel, why don't your mother write to Harry? I surely hope it isn't on my account for he feels so badly and then too I can't tell you how much I want to know and love you all. My own mother is dead and I have no sisters or brothers so look forward to sharing Red's family. We planned to go back this winter but have put it off until next summer or fall. By that time Miss Harriet will be

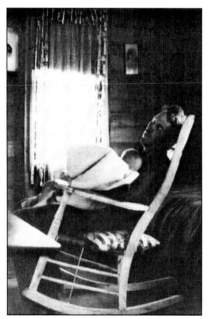

bigger. She's only two weeks old now but badly spoiled.

Red is rocking Baby but tells me to hurry as it is getting late. Please write soon as we watch for your letters on every mail. "Duclair, Mont." is our new address. It is a post-office just started only a mile from me.

Lovingly, Mabel

Harry was a wonderful husband and father. He helped around the house and didn't expect to be waited on. He was a good cook – for a man – and cleaned the dishes and hung laundry. He loved Harriet. Every night when he came home he would scoop up the baby, sit down in the rocking chair, and rock her to sleep while singing a lullaby. He frequently fell asleep before the baby. One of my favorite possessions is a photo of him rocking the baby and sleeping himself.

Autumn came and went like a whirlwind. Harry was busy every day with harvesting and preparing fields for planting the winter wheat. The war in Europe left the world depending on American grains and the U.S. government had guaranteed a price of over two dollars a bushel. In October I wrote in my diary, "The grain on the 'Upper Ranch' as we call Harry's place, is all threshed and we got 342 bu. flax and 110 bu. of wheat." The grains on my land did well, too, producing 400 bushels of oats and 370 bushels of barley. Harry and I were very happy with our harvest. It was easily the most profitable year either of us had seen.

Everyone wanted to clear new acreage and plant as much winter wheat as possible before the cold weather set in. Consequently, Harry and his crew were plowing, discing, and planting from sunup to sundown, seven days a week. In addition to helping others, Harry also wanted to increase our own acreage of grain. Adding his 160 acres to my holdings resulted in our owning over 1,000 acres of land. Some of it was in Father's name, but, of course, we worked his land, too. Harry was eager to get it under the plow and worked late into the night when he could. November 1916 marked a milestone in my life in Montana. I could vote. I could only vote for offices for the state of Montana, but it seemed only a matter of time before women's suffrage would be approved nationwide. I was proud to vote for Jeannette Rankin and send her to Washington as the first female member of the House of Representatives. I supported Woodrow Wilson, even though I couldn't vote for him. I felt he had done a good job keeping us out of the war in Europe.

There was another issue on the ballot I was much more ambivalent about. The Women's Christian Temperance Movement had pushed through a referendum to vote on prohibiting alcohol in Montana. Both Father and Harry were dead set against it.

"Their ideas are ridiculous," said Father, never being shy about expressing his opinion. "Every member of the Elks will vote no, I can promise you that!"

I felt it was a bit silly because there was no way to enforce it out on the prairie, but stories from the mining towns around Butte – where miners would waste their pay on cheap whiskey, abuse their wives and children, and fail to go to work the next day – convinced me to vote yes. The measure passed. Starting in 1918 Montana would join a growing list of states with prohibition laws.

Father shook his head in disgust. "Well, guess I'll be making more trips to Canada in the future."

We had an excellent harvest. Even though I had been slowed by my pregnancy for much of the year Harry managed to work my land and his without many problems. In addition, he was still able to bring in some extra money helping others with their harvest. Still, I was surprised when he announced, "Mabel, I'm going to buy a new gasoline tractor and plow. It will cost over $2000 but I think I can repay the loan in a couple of years if grain prices stay as high as they are right now. I can probably work twice as much land with a new engine."

I was surprised. Harry was a bit of an Irish tightwad and was hesitant to go into debt. He had already shocked me earlier in the year by going to an auction and coming home with three cows and two horses. We needed them, but it was unusual to see him spend so much at one time.

"You're going to spend $2000. Really? I'm surprised, but I can't argue. I know you have researched it and looked at all the options. If you are going to spend that much money it must be important."

"We aren't rich, but we're doing okay. This year's harvest was the best I've had and I was able to save much of what we made. I've already checked and the bank will give me a loan to buy the tractor. I think we have to do it."

A week later he returned from Chinook on top of his new tractor, looking proud as a peacock as he rode into the yard. We had also negotiated a lease of the section to the east of our ranch for five years. This was designated for the township school, but until one was built the land was open for use. Harry went right to work with his new tractor and plow turning the soil and preparing it for next spring. He wanted to plant as much as possible with grain prices at wartime highs.

Harry driving his tractor with Charles on his lap

We hosted a festive Thanksgiving dinner and Harry invited some of his bachelor friends. The Slonakers came over and Bessie and I cooked up a huge feast. We had roast duck and goose the men had shot. We had potatoes, onions, beets, green beans, and carrots from our gardens, and Bessie and I cooked five berry pies. Her children played with Harriet. The adults ate, talked, and laughed most of the night. It was a wonderful day.

We stayed on the ranch through the winter and only visited Havre occasionally. When we were in town we stayed at Father's apartment since he had gone to Seattle to visit relatives and enjoy the milder weather. I visited old friends, who all wanted to see baby Harriet and hear about life on the prairie. I told everyone Harry and I were married in December of 1915 and Harriet was Harry's child. No one ever questioned me. I did not see any of Leo's family, nor did I want to. None of my friends asked about Leo. He had disappeared from my life, and that was exactly the way I wanted it.

Harry and I went to the Elks New Year's Eve dance to welcome in 1917, but it wasn't the same. My interests had changed – I didn't need the dances, card parties, endless dinners, or evenings of small talk to make me happy. I still enjoyed a good movie and good music, but I was happiest staying home with Harry and Harriet and discussing our future. My life and needs had changed and I was convinced they had changed for the better. I had never been happier.

A few days later we were waiting for the eastbound train to take us to Chinook where we would pick up our wagon and team for the ride to the ranch. When the train arrived a young girl stepped off wearing a beautiful silk dress, lace, high boots, a fashionable hat, and a pearl necklace. Her makeup was perfect and not one hair was out of place. Her chin was held high and she appeared to be looking over everyone else in the station. A porter toting a large trunk followed her.

As she walked past me I must have inadvertently stared in her direction. Harry noticed my reaction and said, "Mabel – What are you staring at?"

"Myself. Myself seven years ago. She is what I was when I first came to Montana."

"I didn't know you then," said Harry. "Were you really that stuffed up?"

I was remembering my first trip to Havre. "Oh, I'm afraid so. I wore a fine ivory colored silk dress, had my hair up in a perfect Pompadour and I even carried a small lacy umbrella. I must have been a sight. I'm surprised nobody laughed at me."

Harry started laughing. "Well, I think I'm glad I didn't know you then. I like the way you are now."

I chuckled a bit, too, thinking back on my first visit to Montana. "Harry dear, I've come a long way in the past few years. I think of my childhood in Melrose – I had everything. I had fancy dresses and my hair was always perfectly done up. I knew everyone in town and was socially connected. My grandparents and my parents were community leaders. We had money. Everything was easy."

"So, do you miss it?" was all Harry said.

I continued like I hadn't heard him. "We moved to Grand Forks and I was a high school whiz. I got good grades, played on the basketball team, and was a class officer. I went to college. Once again, Mother made sure I was properly dressed, spoke well, and had connections. Father continued to make good money and kept us in comfortable homes and surroundings."

Harry did not say anything and let me talk.

"We came to Havre and lived in a comfortable house. Father immediately made all the right connections. My life consisted of playing cards, going to dances, plays, and movies, staying up late, and occasionally doing some small work for Father. We claimed our land primarily because Father thought it would be fun to have a piece of the prairie as a hobby and an investment.

"Then everything changed. Mother's death created a huge hole in our lives. Father changed, became moody and more isolated. I had lost my best friend and guide. I moved to the prairie but really didn't know what I was doing. I tried to make a go of it and still keep my social lifestyle and my city friends. Leo was there, but now I realize he wasn't really there. Then he left and you appeared. You saved me."

Harry was humbled. "I don't know if I saved you, or you saved me. I'm just a lucky guy in the right place at the right time to get a wonderful woman."

"No, you saved me," I continued. "I didn't realize how much I loved the land and the ranch until you came along. Tonight, as I was talking to all my old city friends, I realized how much my life has changed. I don't need the fancy hair, makeup, and clothes. I'm much more comfortable in my farming dress with dirty hands and short hair. I don't like the hustle and bustle of the city. I love the pace and work at the homestead. And you are the one who made me realize it. Thank you. I love you."

Later in the day, we braved the cold and mud on our way to the ranch. I was home and happier than I had ever been in my life.

Proving Up: 1917

January and February 1917 were bitter cold, but we were warm and cozy in our well-built house. We still had plenty to do, milking the cows, caring for the horses, keeping the well from freezing, cleaning the house, and, of course, taking care of the baby. Every day we had to "walk the ropes" as we called it. Harry had strung lines to the barn, the chicken coop, and the outhouse to guide us through the snowdrifts in case of a blizzard. It was good preparation, as the winter weather produced some violent storms which kept us housebound for days. We would go to the barn to do our chores then return back to the house. That was the limit of our daily movement. In January the winds blew fierce and the temperature dropped to minus thirty-eight degrees for over three days. We could only venture out for a few minutes at a time. Fortunately, the barn was close enough to get to without developing frostbite. The animal heat kept the barn warm, so once we got there we completed all the chores so we wouldn't have to return until the next day.

Spending most of the day in the cabin gave us time to talk and dream of the future. Our talks continually revolved around going back to Michigan to visit the Greens and introduce me to the family. Naturally, the winter was the only time we could travel and leave the ranch, but it wasn't possible that winter. Not only did we have a small baby, but also our bank account was very low on funds. It didn't prevent us from pining for a chance to go. We put it off and thought, "Maybe next year."

Baby Harriet grew rapidly and was the center of our attention. Letters to Michigan bragged about how quickly she learned to walk and talk. Comments such as, "Oh, she is so sweet! Every day she springs some new trick on us. Every time I touch the piano she keeps up a little sing song as long as I play," were common. Another letter exclaims, "She is getting so smart. Does or says some new cute thing every day." We obviously were very proud parents.

Spring came early as the Chinook winds came from the south in April and helped thaw the prairie soils. Harry immediately got to work getting our land plowed and ready for seed. We used the leased school section for pasture. We had ten horses and eighteen head of cattle to graze there. The government continued to encourage clearing more land and planting more crops. Our increased acreage should have been enough to keep Harry busy, but he continued to take on jobs helping others plow, harrow, plant, and harvest throughout the growing season.

Spring also brought Father as a permanent houseguest. He had filed a homestead claim for the quarter section to our southwest, but had not lived there or improved the land. We talked him into building a small shack so he could meet the residency requirement and Harry worked the land, so it would be cultivated and improved in accordance with the rules. Father would stay there occasionally, when the weather was nice, or when he just wanted to get away for a while, but most of the time he stayed with us.

He was sixty-four years old and starting to slow down. He had not taken good care of his health living by himself and he was not well. Harry and I suggested he get out of his apartment in Havre so he could be near us. He could help with little things around the farm and watch baby Harriet while we worked in the fields. While he could be helpful, he was still cantankerous and unpredictable. He had never lived on a ranch and sometimes when things went wrong he would find fault with one of us. It would cause Harry and me to be hurt for a while. Father could be loving and supportive, then the next minute be angry about the littlest thing and quarrel with both of us. His moods frequently affected Harry and me. Often it ended up with all of us yelling at each other.

One day, while Father was out, Harry said to me, "Mabel, if there is trouble of any kind – from something other people say, or something we do, or even grief and hard times – it will do one of two things. Either it will drive us apart, or it will make us closer together. But it is up to us – and us alone – to decide which it does."

I have never forgotten what he said. If something came up, or if Father's mood changes annoyed us, we would remind each other, "let everything else go hang that could hurt or separate us." We expected to stick together as long as God let us.

"War! We've declared war on Germany!" It was April 8, 1917. Ray Croft came back from a trip to Chinook with word the United States was at war with Germany. The entire community was abuzz with the news.

"The telegraph operator in Chinook said Congress voted to go to war two days ago," said Ray. "The President said the United States had to make the world safe for democracy. I like his thinking. He has already asked for volunteers for the army. Some boys in Chinook were talking about going right away."

"Well, I know I'm too old for the military, but I'm all for supporting our boys and the war effort," said Elmer Slonaker. "At least it will keep crop prices high. It should be good for us. I'm already thinking of clearing more land and planting more."

We hadn't heard much news about the European war, but when we did it wasn't good. People had been anticipating America's declaration of war for months. Germany had resumed unrestricted submarine warfare in January. Then, in February, it was discovered Germany had tried to convince Mexico to enter the war on their side in order to win back the American Southwest. Both events brought screams of anger and protest, especially in the Great Plains. The submarine warfare slowed our shipping of grain to Europe, which impacted profits on the Montana farms. Any discussion of Mexico trying to conquer lands in the west was met with anger and seen as a direct challenge to the sovereignty of the United States.

"I don't like the idea of going to war," I stated. "But I guess Germany has been asking for it. Seems they have been getting more and more belligerent in the last few months. I don't like it, but I guess we've got to do it."

"How did our new female Congresswoman vote?" Bessie Slonaker asked.

"She voted 'No.' Said she couldn't vote for war regardless of the reasons. She was one of only eight representatives voting 'No'," said Ray.

"That sounds like something a woman would do," said Bob Robertson, one of the more outspoken opponents of women getting the right to vote. "Just like I predicted – she was soft when the going got tough."

I ignored his cynicism and bit my tongue. It wasn't the right time or place for an argument. I proudly said, "Well, I admire her bravery. I'm sure everyone was pressuring her to vote for war, but she stuck to her principles and voted her conscience. It must have been tough."

Ray changed the topic, almost like he didn't hear what I was saying. "There is also talk about instituting a draft system to boost the size of our army. The President says we are going to need over a million men and our army is nowhere near big enough."

Harry had been standing near the back of the crowd, but now he spoke up. "A draft? I guess he doesn't figure we will get enough volunteers. It sure won't be good if all our farm help is drafted into the service. This could change a lot of things."

In June the President signed the Selective Service Act and started drafting men eighteen to thirty years old. Harry did his duty and went to Chinook to register at the Blaine County Selective Service Office, but agricultural workers were exempt from the first call-up, so there wasn't any worry about his leaving. The government realized for us to win they were going to have to protect our agricultural output. Harry was glad to continue farming. "I'm helping the war effort," he would say with a smile. I was just glad he didn't have to go overseas and fight someone else's war.

A few weeks later we were shopping in Chinook and noticed a crowd at the train station. Seventy-one Blaine County boys were shipping out for the war. Until then the war had been half a world away and only a distant news item for us. Now it became more personal. We knew many of the families involved and felt their concern and love as their sons went off to war. Shortly afterward I wrote, "I never in the world would stand it to see Harry go. Why even when he's gone three or four hours I nearly lose my mind."

Harry's older brother, Frank, however, decided to enlist. It was never clear why he volunteered. He was thirty-two which was quite old for an enlistee. Harry thought it was a way for Frank to get away from his mother and see the world. Sister Hazel wrote Frank felt it was the patriotic thing to do. Whatever his reasoning, it caused more tension and anxiety in the family.

While 1917 was tumultuous politically and overseas, it was also a busy year at the Z/T Ranch.

By the spring of the year I was ready to prove up my claims. I had now lived there long enough to meet the homestead requirement to live on the land and cultivate it for three years. I knew I had not been on the land long enough in 1913, but felt I had met all the requirements from March 1914 to March 1917. The process was a bit complicated but necessary. First I had to file a "Notice of Intention to Make Proof" which I did in March. Then it had to be published in the Chinook and Havre newspapers for five weeks in case there were any conflicting claims or outstanding debt. Finally, on June seventh, Harry and I went to the Havre Land Office to file the paperwork for my final proof. We needed two witnesses to verify I had lived on the land and improved it, so Pete Peterson and Jesse Moreland went with us and signed affidavits supporting my claims. It then needed to be reviewed by the United States Commissioner of the Havre Land Office, but we didn't foresee any problems.

At the same time, Father and I submitted applications for the final proof on the 480 acres claimed in our names under the Desert Land Act. These proofs had been held up by Mother's untimely death. One claim of 160 acres was made in her name. It had to be transferred to my name, which extended the timeframe for filing. The requirements were a bit different, since I wasn't required to live on the land, only irrigate it and improve it. That was easy, since Father had been working to divert the water from the reservoir to the land ever since we arrived on the land. Pete and Jesse were also willing to be witnesses for those claims.

I walked out of the office and hugged Harry with excitement. "Just think, four years ago I was standing in line at the Land Office when I first saw you. I admit I was bluffing back then. I really didn't know what I was in for. I've learned so much and done so much since then. With any luck I will have the deed to my land within a couple months."

But it wasn't going to be easy and only got more complicated.

Ten days later I received a letter from the Havre office of the Department of the Interior rejecting my application for final proof because I did not show evidence of sufficient cultivation in 1914. I was shocked and scared.

"Harry, what am I going to do? If my claim is rejected I could lose the land. Someone else could claim it and kick us off." I was so upset I did not read all the form.

Harry remained calm and read the letter. "It says you have thirty days to appeal their decision. Why would they say you had insufficient cultivation for 1914?"

"Well, to begin with, I was pregnant and had a miscarriage. But I'm not going to tell them that. I plowed forty acres and planted ten, but it was a dry and hot year. Nothing grew. If I had worked hard and tried to bring in a crop it would have been worth nothing anyways. By the end of the summer the grain was stunted and there was nothing to harvest. You remember, don't you?"

"Yes, it was a bad year. You did plant a crop though. That should account for something, even if you didn't get to harvest it."

So in July, we went back to the commissioner's office to file our appeal. I testified I had planted ten acres of flax and plowed thirty acres with the intention of planting grains there. However, it had been so hot and dry no crops grew throughout the Cherry Ridge area. I then pointed out I had planted and harvested the land the following year.

"Besides," I told the commissioner, "the law only says the land has to be cultivated. It doesn't say it has to be successfully harvested. I always thought if I summer fallowed the land in preparation for planting next year it was sufficient cultivation to comply with the law. Doesn't it qualify that I cleared it and tried to grow a crop, even if it was unsuccessful?"

Commissioner Kenyon looked up from my paperwork. "You have a valid point Mrs. Greene. It was a bad year, but the rules are you are supposed to grow a crop."

"I tried, but there was nothing to harvest." I was disturbed by his attitude but tried to stay calm.

"Okay, I believe you made a serious attempt to grow a crop. I will recommend approval of your appeal. But it will have to go up the chain, first to the General Land Office in Helena, then to Washington D.C. I think everything will be fine."

"And how long will it take? I would like to get this done."

"Be patient, Mrs. Greene," he said calmly. "This may take a couple months, but I think you have a good argument and your proof will be accepted. I don't think you have anything to worry about."

"And what about my proof for the desert land I have?" I asked.

"Oh, it looks fine, but I'm going to keep it all together to send to Washington. You don't want it to get separated because it could get lost and you would have to file everything all over again."

I was relieved to hear that. "Okay, thank you. We will wait to hear from you."

As the summer went on it became more urgent for my claim to be proved up successfully. It was another hot, dry summer and the crops were suffering. Near the end of July a temperature of 108 degrees was recorded in the shade. It had never been that hot in the seven years I had been in Montana. The heat continued with a string of days in the nineties. If the dry weather continued, we would have no crop and it would be one more insufficient year for our proof. In a letter to sister Hazel, Harry wrote, "Our crops are all burned up – will get nothing out of our acres ..." If my appeal was not accepted, we might have to start over.

The drought and threat of losing the crops also put a huge financial pinch on Harry and me. Harry had gone into debt to buy the new engine with the expectation he would be able to harvest at least as much grain as last year – if not more. The calculations he had given the bank to secure the loan were unreachable and he was afraid the bank might call the loan.

One of the first things we sacrificed to save money was a planned trip to Michigan. We had written expressing a desire to return east for Christmas, however, we soon gave up on the idea. In a letter to Hazel we admitted, "We put so much into cattle and the engine. We will surely come if we can find a way and I'm not going to stop hoping. That's all we talk about or live for."

In an attempt to consolidate our holdings and also take advantage of decent land prices Harry sold his 160 acres of land to the northeast of our ranch. It was good land but was too far from our ranch. Harry got a decent price and was able to pay off the $1600 mortgage on that section and part of the loan on the tractor, but after making those payments we were still broke. We talked about selling some of my land, but it wasn't possible until my proof was approved and I had the Land Patent in hand. And my proof was still being held up on technicalities.

The entire community was suffering in the heat. We stuck together and worked through it. Harry did his best to help irrigate wherever possible. Our little reservoir wasn't big enough to help other homesteaders, but it did provide a nice spot for swimming and cooling off in the evening. We often had four or five families meeting at the pond to relax a bit, share news, and clean up after a long day in the fields.

August was Harriet's first birthday and Harry surprised me by buying a gentle little pony for her.

"Harry, it's ridiculous to buy Harriet a pony. She can't ride yet," I said with a laugh.

"It won't be long before she can," he crowed. "I'll give her riding lessons myself. She is around the animals all day. She should learn how to master a horse. I intend to buy a horse for each of our children."

Tootsie – as the pony was named – became a family favorite and would follow Harriet around the yard like a big dog. We all loved her.

As feared it was a terrible year for crops throughout the community. Harry helped our neighbors bring in whatever they could, usually for no charge, but no one was able to harvest enough to make a trip to the grain elevator worthwhile. We brought in some vegetables, potatoes, enough grain for ourselves, alfalfa for the animals, but nothing worth anything at market. It was a quiet, but thoughtful autumn.

In November I received more bad news on my proof. A letter came from the General Land Office in Helena delaying my appeal.

"Now they want to investigate my claim further," I said with disgust. "This letter says 'the chief of field division has requested the final certificate be withheld until field investigation has been made.' My God, Harry, this could take months. I'm getting very frustrated with the whole process. What do they think I've been doing out here for the last four-and-a-half years!"

Harry was mad, too, but knew it wouldn't do any good to get me more riled up. He tried to be reasonable. "You're right, it is frustrating and irritating, but there isn't anything we can do. We have to be patient, Mabel, and let the bureaucracy run its course. It will take time, but as long as our family is together we will figure out a way to get by."

"Speaking of family," I said quietly and cheerfully, "I think I'm pregnant."

Harry looked at me and yelled, "What! Why didn't you say so? When are you due?"

"Well, I didn't want to say anything because I think I'm only a couple months and the right time didn't really present itself, but this seems as good a time as any. As I figure it, I'm probably due in the summer – mid-July."

"Wonderful. So we don't have to moan about the proof inspection. We will have a bigger, better family. That's all that matters. I do love you Mabel, and I love children. I want to have a whole brood running around this ranch."

"Okay, okay – let's take care of one at a time," and I laughed at his silliness.

The inspector from the government's General Land Office made his inspection of our ranch in late November. It seemed strange for him to come so late in the year, since all the crops were in and the fields plowed. But we wanted to get the process over with and did not want him to wait until spring, so we were happy when he showed up. His inspection was very cursory and I felt he was only going through the motions to satisfy the requirement to make the inspection. After less than two hours of riding the range with Harry and asking a few questions, he prepared to leave.

As he collected his paperwork and warmed up a bit before heading back to Havre he told me, "You have a nice place here, Mrs. Greene. I will recommend approval of your appeal and the final certificate should be issued. I have listed your yearly crop yield and the improvements you have made to the place. I am stating the improvements you made are valued at $1,500. Does that sound fair to you?"

I thought it was wonderful news, "Yes, it sounds excellent. Thank you."

"I'm sorry we had to put you through this hassle," he said, "but there have been a lot of false claims and testimonies submitted with final proofs lately. A number of homesteaders have not worked their claims and have not been physically residing on the land."

I was curious. "Really? I guess there are some folks just out to get the land. That's too bad."

"Oh, you'd be surprised at the lengths some are taking to try and beat the system. With more and more people coming to the plains it's not unusual to see land speculators trying to get as much as they can as cheap as they can."

He shook his head in mock disbelief. "For example, there was a fellow who plowed around the edge of his land because the law said you had to plow 'around ten acres' to qualify. Many have tried building small houses no bigger than dog houses to qualify as their residence."

Harry and I laughed. "Unbelievable. I guess I can see why you have to check all the claims carefully."

"Yep – so the federal government has directed us to be more vigilant and physically examine the claims. Yours is an easy inspection – other than the cold weather. You have obviously lived here, been working the land, and intend to stay here. This will be an easy one to recommend approval on."

"Thank you. It's reassuring to hear. And thank you for the explanation of why we had to go through this. No one has said anything before. It might have given me less anxiety if I knew all this back in July."

He concluded by saying, "I'll get this report in soon. It's almost time for the Christmas holidays, so it might not get approved in Helena until January. Then it will go to Washington D.C. So I wouldn't look for anything until the spring at the latest."

"Thanks again," I said. "Have safe travels back to town."

Winter on the prairie was always fierce and unpredictable. We did not have much snow – it was still dry in the winter – but it was extremely cold with temperatures routinely at negative twenty degrees and winds blasting out of the north. In a letter back to Michigan we explained the weather on a weekend trip to Havre. "When we drove in it was thirty-eight degrees below but we were cozy and warm as could be in our covered sleigh. Coming back a 'chinook' warm wind was blowing and it was thawing."

But we made it through the winter without incident. Spring came with its perpetual promise of warmth and growth. It always brought hope of a better crop.

At the end of March we received the letter we had been waiting for from the Department of Interior, General Land Office stating "the final certificate ... will be promptly placed in the channel leading to patent" of the land and give us a deed. It was a long, frustrating process but on August 24, 1918, I had a Final Patent signed by President Woodrow Wilson for my little piece of Montana prairie. I felt more secure than ever.

Family and Farming

Charles Richmond Greene was born July 24, 1918. This time I was more prepared and moved to Chinook a week before the baby was due. He was a restless one though and arrived three days early. Harry was ecstatic to have a son. We named him in honor of our fathers.

"We now have an heir to the family name," he boisterously exclaimed with pride.

Father was also busting with pride. "A boy to carry on the Richmond line, too. I didn't want to be the last to bear the Richmond name. Even though it's only his middle name, it will continue our family legacy. Harry, we can teach him to ride, fish, and shoot. He will be the best hunter around. Oh, a boy is so wonderful."

Four days later we were back at the ranch and Harry was again busy in the fields. It had been a good year with adequate rains and the crops were progressing well. Harry continued to rent land on the school section next to us and we had over two hundred acres planted in flax, barley, and wheat. He had almost forty acres in alfalfa and over a hundred fallowed for the next season. There was plenty of land for the livestock to graze. He also continued to take the tractor and wagon to neighboring fields and work for hire.

While Harry busied himself in the field, I was busy with two babies. Father was living with us in the summer and helped with the children. Sometimes though, he was a bigger problem than the little ones. He could be very demanding. Harriet, who was almost two, loved her baby brother. She treated him as her doll and wanted to help me with everything from diaper changes to feeding. Of course, since I was nursing, the feeding part was a bit complicated for her to understand. She would help me in the vegetable garden by pulling up whatever weed I pointed out. She also enjoyed watching Charles on the blanket while I worked.

The war was still raging in Europe. The local Montana papers carried little news of the war, since American boys were not yet involved in the fighting, but we heard plenty from family letters. Frank had been in Fort Polk, Louisiana for the last year, but was preparing to ship out soon. Frank wrote to Harry and said, "Looks like we will be going to Ireland first to do supply work. After that I have no idea what will happen or where we will be going."

The war helped keep grain prices high as we continued to be the source of food for Europe. And it also helped – along with Charles's birth – bring about reconciliation between Mother Green and Harry. After Charles was born she wrote a letter of congratulations to Harry, which was the first we had received directly from her since he had announced our engagement.

Harry was happy and relieved to hear from his mother. "She's finally come around to accepting you, Mabel. I guess she thinks having a grandson named after her husband is more important than the religion thing. I'm so glad to be able to write my family now."

"It seems as if Frank's military service has opened her eyes a bit, too," I mentioned. "She writes a lot about his status and passing on his information."

Harry agreed. "Without a doubt, it has helped. I think it's more important than ever we get back to Michigan this winter to visit the family. It will be good to take the babies and show them off."

"Yes, I think it would be a good time. If the crops come in like you are predicting, we should have enough money."

It was a good harvest season. We had record yields of our flax and barley. Although Harry thought the wheat harvest could have been better, we made a decent profit when we took it all to the railhead in Chinook and shipped it east. The entire Cherry Ridge community had better yields.

In mid-November wonderful news came from Europe. James Furtchbar came running over to our ranch, "The was is over. They've signed an armistice. It went into effect on November eleventh. No more killing."

"Oh – What wonderful news, James." I was very happy. I had not enjoyed hearing war news and stories of all the killing. "Maybe Harry's brother Frank can come home soon."

James added, "They say over six hundred Montana men have been killed and over a thousand have been wounded. And many of the eastern states have higher numbers of killed and wounded. Harry, I hope your brother wasn't injured."

Harry shook his head, "No, I don't think he even got to the front lines. He worked on supplies. I know my parents will be glad to get Frank back to Michigan though." Then Harry, always thinking of the financial advantages, added, "Peace will make it safer to ship our grain to Europe. They will probably need it even more now. Grain prices should continue to be high."

Word of peace in Europe and good crops made for a festive Thanksgiving. Once more, we hosted Thanksgiving dinner with the Slonakers, Crofts, Furchtbars, and Harry's bachelor field hands attending. The women cooked, the men talked politics and farming, and the children ran around the yard chasing animals and having a wonderful time. After a huge feast I played piano while we all sang George M Cohan's *Over There*, and other new songs about the war. It was a wonderful day.

After Charles was born we decided this was the year to make the trip back to Michigan. Of course, we could not leave the ranch during harvest time, but after the harvest was in we began making preparations for the trip. It was late December before Harry got everything in order at the ranch. We boarded the Great Northern No. 2 heading east out of Chinook. Three days later we arrived in Jackson. Harry's younger brother, Riley, met us at the station and took us to the Green farm in Parma.

We were delighted to learn Mother and Father Green had gathered all the family and neighbors for our arrival. Of course, Harry had told me what to expect, but I enjoyed finally getting to know everyone. We talked well into the evening and continued throughout the next day.

I discovered I had a lot in common with Mother Green – her name was Mary Katherine, but I always called her Mother Green. She still would have preferred I was Catholic, but she appreciated how I was hard working, loved her son, and protected my family. Father and Mother Green were second-generation Irish and proud of their heritage. Both the Greens and the Rileys – Mary's maiden name – had emigrated from Ireland in the mid-1800s and settled in Michigan by the end of the Civil War. All of their seven children – except Harry – lived within twenty or thirty miles, so it was a close family. Mother Green was, without a doubt, the dominant personality in the family. If I was going to become part of the family, I had to be accepted by her. By the end of our visit I felt I had succeeded in gaining her trust as a good daughter-in-law.

It was a festive holiday season. Harry took me to all his old haunts and I met some of his old friends. Unfortunately, many had gone off to war. Some had died and the others were still overseas and would not be home until the spring. Most important, though, was my time spent with Harry's family. I had been writing letters to them for two years, but now I could put names and faces together. I especially enjoyed talking to Hazel. She was six years younger than me, but outgoing, cheerful, and full of life. We talked about marriage, children, and family and found we had the same priorities. She was not married, but was seeing a young man and seemed determined he was the man for her.

Harriet loved the Christmas decorations and celebrations. She had never seen anything like them on the prairie and asked hundreds of questions about the tree, the decorations, and the family traditions. She always had an audience of one of the grandparents or aunts and uncles. She quickly became everyone's favorite playmate. Charles, of course, was too young to really understand what was happening, but still demanded everyone's attention when he wanted something. Both children received gifts from the relatives. They got a few toys, but in my opinion, the best gifts were clothing and winter outfits for both of them.

The New Year's celebration was calm in southern Michigan. Parma was a small farm community and did not have a big New Year's gathering. We stayed in and spent the time with family. It was a mild winter in the Midwest and it only made us curious of what winter was like in Montana. I wrote a few letters to Bessie Slonaker, but did not get a reply which told me it was a hard winter and they could not get to the post office.

By the middle of March Harry was ready to return to the ranch. We said our good-byes and promised to return the next winter. We also extracted a few promises from family members to come visit us in Montana. We desperately tried to talk Hazel into coming and taking a teaching position at a school district starting up only fifteen miles away from us but she was in love and wasn't interested.

We took the train to Chicago, switched to a sleeper car and were in Minneapolis the next morning. We stopped there to spend two days with my cousin Carlton. Carlton was my aunt Harriet's only surviving son and the only relative I grew up with. Carlton was married to a beautiful woman whom I immediately took a liking to. He was an entertainment agent and had a growing business of booking actors and actresses in vaudeville shows and theater. He was even starting to get some bookings for his clients on Broadway and in some silent movies. He told us if things continued the way they were he would soon be moving to Chicago for more visibility.

From Minneapolis we went to Melrose. We checked in at the hotel and called the Taylors, who were old family friends. As soon as they came to the hotel they said, "Mabel, you can't stay here, especially with these two darling children. You must come and stay at our house. We want to talk and remember all the old times. Please come over."

I looked up at Harry. "I told you people in Melrose were wonderful." He said, "How can we refuse? Thank you very much." We stayed two wonderful days in my old hometown.

We hired a car and drove around town. I was amazed at how much I remembered and how little things had changed. The downtown was bigger and the city had more people, but the old buildings and streets were the same. I showed Harry where Father's mill had been – it burned down shortly after we moved to Montana – and where we used to live. We also discovered the school Father had built, and I was so proud of, had burned down in 1914. I knew Father would be disappointed when I told him. Around noon we took a quiet trip to Oak Hill Cemetery to visit Mother's grave. It was clean and well cared for, and I wept when I saw it. Harry paid his respects, then took the children for a walk to give me some time at the gravesite.

It was a cold, damp, overcast day. "Oh, Mother," I whispered to her tombstone, "I think of you so often. I want to be the woman you brought me up to be, but I often wonder if I've failed you. So much has happened since you died. Leo left me, Harry came, the babies came, and the ranch is doing okay. It's a struggle, but we are working hard to make it a success. I think of what you taught me every day and try to keep a positive attitude." I was blubbering.

"Mama – if you were here I know you would love Harry. He is such a wonderful man. And you would smother Harriet and Charles with kisses every day. Papa is being good to your memory. He still goes off and hunts and fishes often and he is still consulting for the railroad. Not as much, but enough to make a little extra. And he still can't save money. He makes those risky investments you always hated. He spends it when he gets it. But he's not going to change and I still love him even though he can be exasperating. I sometimes wonder how you put up with him for all those years.

"I think of your words of wisdom every day. I do look ahead and try not to look back at past events. They can't be changed. I want to move on. Thank you for all you taught me. I love you."

I got up and walked around the cemetery. Mother was buried in the Richmond family plot along with the sister I never knew, Harriet. The rest of the Richmonds were there; Father's brother, Reuben, Grandfather, Grandmother, and Great-grandfather Richmond were all there together. The Conner plots were only a few steps away with the graves of Grandfather and Grandmother Conner. Tall oaks and peaceful shrubbery beautifully surrounded the spot. It was a sad place for me, but lovely.

I met Harry at the gate and thanked him for the time alone. He understood and didn't say a word.

The rest of the trip was much more enjoyable. We met old friends of Father's, and Harry, with his laugh and outgoing personality, became friends with most of Melrose instantly. It was a great time.

Two more days on the train brought us to Chinook in the middle of freezing temperatures and a snowstorm, even though it was March thirtieth. It took Harry two hours to hire a car to take us out to the ranch. While waiting I met two neighbor couples at the station. They were also looking for a way to their ranches, so when Harry found a car we all squeezed in. We had six adults, three children, five suitcases, and plenty of groceries. On the way to our ranch we got stuck in the middle of a big puddle of water. One of the fellows unpacked his suitcase, got out a pair of rubber boots, and then carried the men on his back to the high, dry bank. Then they tied a rope to the car and pulled it out. We were dirty and cold when we got home, but were pleasantly surprised to find the neighbors had come in, warmed up the house, and made a welcome home dinner for us. I even found a nice geranium with six beautiful blossoms waiting for me. Again the friendship of the homesteaders of Montana made us realize how lucky we were.

When Father returned from his winter stay in Seattle he immediately started spoiling the children. He took them to his workshop and made small wooden toys while they watched. Charles was crawling and would get into everything in the shop, but Father didn't seem to mind. He took them on horseback rides holding both in his lap while his horse walked around the ranch. Luckily he had an old, quiet horse that needed no guidance since Father usually wasn't holding the reins. The children would laugh and giggle, which only made Father smile more.

Every day Harry awoke before the sun, milked the cows, did the separating, fed the livestock, gathered eggs, and was in the fields before seven. Our hired hand had quit and gone back east, so Harry and a neighbor worked together, alternating between fields every other day. He continued to increase the amount of land used each year. He planted almost five hundred acres in wheat, flax, and rye, and had another five hundred acres for pasture. He went to Canada again to get the seed wheat, since it was only $2.02 a pound compared to $3.00 in Chinook. The weather looked good, prices were high, and again we were optimistic of a good harvest. Of course, this was before the summer heat, which always determined success or failure in the fields.

The children were getting bigger and Father was around more to watch them, which allowed me to work in the fields more. I had helped Harry prior to Harriet's birth and had always loved being in the fields, but had not done much in the last two years. Now I could get out behind our four-horse team and help with the plowing and harrowing. In one letter to Hazel I described my fieldwork by saying, "You should have seen me harrowing today. When I came in I was surely a Dusty Lady. I love to be out in the field and before Harriet was born I was with Harry on the machinery all the time."

Summer brought some sort of epidemic sweeping through Cherry Creek and the surrounding communities. It hit the menfolk hard. Harry, Papa, and Charles were all bedridden with it. For some reason, neither Harriet nor I became sick. Harry and Papa had a tough week but were eventually fine. Poor little Charles however, being only two, became violently ill and could not keep down any food. We feared for his life. The doctor visited from Chinook, but there wasn't much he, or anyone, could do. Many other children in the area were sick and the doctor said a few in Havre had died. We tried to control Charles' fever, gave him water, and did our best to keep him comfortable. Finally, after ten scary days, he came around. He still needed plenty of love and care, but he started eating again. When he complained of still being hungry after a big breakfast we knew he would be fine. By the end of the week he was walking, jabbering away, and being himself. We counted our blessings.

I updated sister Hazel on his health. "Charles is surely cute. He walks all over and goes like the wind, too. He surely bosses the whole bunch and tries to make us all stand around. We say every day how we wish Dad Green could see him. He does so many cute things."

Our little community of homesteaders continued to grow. While there were a few new landowners most of the growth was due to more and more children being born. It seemed everyone had a couple of children with more on the way. A one-room school was started about a half mile away on the school section to the southeast of our ranch. In less than a year the student population increased from six to eight. The wife of a rancher near DuClair taught the class but there was talk in the community of hiring a full-time teacher. I was anxious to have a good teacher by the time Harriet started in a couple more years.

Also, we started a little Sunday School. It was a small neighborhood affair with no formal pastor or denomination, but we enjoyed it. We gathered at a small church started by the Quakers in Cherry Ridge. It had a nice little pump organ I played for the service. I also took a turn teaching the youngsters' class. Then, after our service, someone would host a dinner gathering for everyone. It was always the same people. It was great fun. When it was my turn to host we had twenty-eight for supper. It was a wonderful way to bring a bit of culture to the prairie and to enjoy our neighbors' company.

August was hot and dry. The temperature was above ninety for almost two whole weeks, with a couple days of one hundred degrees mixed in. The crops were almost ready to harvest, in spite of the heat. Harry watched them daily for signs of distress or drought. "This heat has taken its toll on the crops. Everyone is complaining about the drought and saying their fields are burning up. The north fields have almost nothing salvageable, but we are doing okay here. If we can get about two more weeks with decent weather we should be fine," he said. "I can harvest and thresh and we will still have a good harvest."

Two days later Harry came back from milking the cows and said, "Storm's comin.' I can feel it and the livestock are jumpy. The horses have come in close to the barn. That's not like them."

I looked outside. It was only seven in the morning, but it was already hot and sticky. It was clear overhead, but huge thunderclouds were forming on the western horizon. "It's going to rain somewhere for sure," I said. "Think it will miss us?"

Harry shook his head. "Can't say. Guess it could, but it seems big enough to get the whole county. Not good."

We watched the clouds build all morning. Harry inspected the outbuildings to make sure everything was secure. By ten o'clock the clouds were piling up in the southwest, turning heavy and dark, and rolling over each other racing to get to the High Plains. There was nothing we could do except watch and pray it passed us by. "If it's only rain we should be okay," Harry said. "The crops are strong enough to stand up to rain. But if it's hail ..." He couldn't finish the sentence because a huge clap of thunder rolling across the prairie signaled the beginning of the storm.

"Looks like it's raining on Slonaker's south fields. It's coming fast Mabel."

Harry was interrupted again by a loud thunderclap. Bolts of lightning lite up the dark, heavy sky.

"Time to get the children in. It's going to be a big one," shouted Harry over the noise of another thunderclap. We gathered the children and ran inside the house. Just as we did it started to hail. First it was little flicks of ice, but suddenly the whole house shook with the thundering drumbeat of hailstones on our roof and windows. When we looked out the ground was covered with hailstones, many over an inch in diameter.

Harry sat down, put his head in his hands, and shook his head in disbelief. "It will be gone, I'm sure. This will kill our grain. It will beat it flat and it will be worthless. This should have been our best year yet. Now I don't know if we'll get anything. It's crazy. You can't get ahead out here. Something always works against you." He was in more despair than I had ever seen him. The joyful, optimistic man I knew was nowhere to be found. I took the children to the back bedroom and left him alone. I knew there was nothing I could say to help his mood.

The storm lasted less than thirty minutes before racing off to the east, but the damage was done. In the evening we walked the fields. The southern and western fields were hard hit and there was nothing of any value left. The wheat and rye were bent and broken right at ground level. The hail had pounded the stalks into the ground. All we could do was pick up bits of grain to feed the livestock, but there was nothing to harvest. The fields on the north side had been spared a bit. There were about twenty acres of flax that could be harvested and taken to market, but it would barely pay for the money Harry had put into seed. We were devastated. Harry walked in circles looking at the damaged crops and mumbling to himself. He was totally lost. I wanted to cheer him up but was too distraught myself. Neither of us knew what to do next.

The next morning Harry went over some figures to calculate our loss. After about an hour he looked up and said, "It's going to be tight this winter. We've got a lot of debts to pay. I still owe on the tractor and the new rake. We also owe for the seed and fertilizer I bought in Canada. I can probably talk the bank into extending my loan a bit longer. I know one thing for sure – there won't be any trip to Michigan this winter. We are probably going to have to stick it out here and save what we can."

I came over and put my hand on his shoulder in support. "We can do it. We've overcome plenty of obstacles before.

209

And we've had our share. We can do it again. How much can you make hiring out to help folks bring in their harvest?"

Harry was deep in thought. "Well, from the size of the storm, I'm not sure anyone around here will have anything left to harvest. I might have to go to another county to find decent fields to work."

"If that's what you have to do, then that's what you have to do. The children and I will be okay. Father should be back soon and he can help around here." Father had been away on a consulting job for the railroad and was scheduled to be back by the weekend.

Harry looked up and smiled. "That's what I love about you, Mabel. Many wives would be miserable in this situation, but you look for a way out. You're right. We have overcome some big obstacles. We'll get by. As long as we have each other, the children, and the farm, we'll be fine. We'll just have to work a little harder."

We always tried to be optimistic in our letters to Michigan. We figured there was no need to worry them about things they had no control over. After the hailstorm Harry wrote to explain why we wouldn't be visiting in the winter. He found it hard to stay upbeat. "We lost a lot in the storm, but will get by. We've got to stay with the land now until we pay off our debts or we will lose what we have. Believe me it wouldn't take much to lose it. We would like to come home but are not able to this year. But prospects look pretty good for next year."

We were able to harvest more than we thought after the hailstorm, but it was barely enough to cover our outstanding debt. It was going to be a tight winter. Harry was raising horses and had thirty head to sell in order to supplement his farming income. Prices were low at the auction, so he didn't get as much as he wanted. He decided to keep some of the horses through the winter in hopes prices would be better next spring. Therefore, he had to make sure we got a good crop of hay and alfalfa to feed the livestock through the winter.

It was a bitter, cold winter, with temperatures occasionally reaching fifty below zero. Any attempt to go outside became an adventure. The Dalkes, neighborhood friends, had a big birthday party and invited everyone in the Cherry Hill community. We had a wonderful time, but when it was time to go, we found almost two feet of snow had fallen since we had left home and it was still coming down. We decided to spend the night with the Dalkes and went home the next day.

The winter was so cold we rarely went out. Harry would care for the livestock, which usually took three or four hours every morning. After those chores were done, it was pretty boring sitting in the house trying to stay busy. Father was with us during the winter and was always complaining Harry didn't know what he was talking about. He wouldn't go out himself to show the way, but he loved to bicker and whine and tell us what to do.

We played cards throughout the day to stay busy. Harry and Father would often bet with the loser doing chores around the house. Father seemed to win most, so when either of us beat him, it was a big deal. The winner would hoot and crow and tease the loser for the rest of the day. I'm not sure who was the bigger bragger, but Harry loved it when he beat Father and always let him know it.

"Ha – got you this time Edmond," Harry started after one particularly long game. "I guess I know who is killing the chicken for dinner. Better get to it, I don't want my dinner to be late."

Father hated to lose. "You were lucky this time. One more hand to decide who has to pluck it and clean it. You in?"

Harry shook his head and laughed. "Oh no – that was all included in the first bet. Get your coat on and get out there and get my dinner. Don't be getting a skinny one either. I want the fattest hen you can find. I don't beat you often, so I've got to take advantage of this."

A Dangerous Prank

Spring came late in 1920. It seemed the winter cold and blasting winds would never let up, but finally, in late April a warm Chinook wind started thawing the prairie. Suddenly everything was green and the eternal hope of spring returned. Harriet and Charles played in the yard and chased the chickens and geese. Harry and I went for a lovely horseback ride while Papa watched the children. It felt good to be out and be part of the blooming of a new season.

An hour into our ride we paused on a hilltop overlooking our fields and Harry shared some thoughts, "With the war over and Europe's fields recovering we will lose our market. Prices are bound to fall so I've got to put in more crops in order to get the same money we got in the war years. It's a vicious cycle. I don't see how we can get ahead. Still, I love it here and wouldn't want to be doing anything else."

I looked around the fields and said, "I understand your frustration. I feel the same way. It's hard work and we don't seem to be getting ahead, but I've never been happier. We have good friends, two wonderful children, and each other. We can make it work."

Ever since Harriet's birth Bessie Slonaker had become my closest friend. We had so much in common. She and

Elmer were about the same age as Harry and me. She had three children, Olive, Les, and Leland, who were only a bit older than Harriet and Charles. Our houses were about a quarter mile apart, but on the prairie, that was close. We could wave to each other when we were out and the children would run back and forth to play. The children were outside continuously throughout the summer and either I would go to Bessie's, or she would come over to our place for coffee and conversation every day. Many days, after Harry and Elmer came in from the fields, we would eat the evening meal together. If they were at our house I would play piano and we would all sing and talk until late into the night.

Our little prairie community continued to work together and help each other. When the Peterson barn blew down in a storm, we all helped with a community barn-raising. Twenty men put the barn up while the women prepared a huge meal to enjoy when the work was done. By the end of the day we were laughing and eating and congratulating each other on how good the barn looked. Camaraderie and friendship were commonplace on the prairie.

It wasn't all work. We had our share of entertainment. On weekends neighbors would hitch up their wagons and ride ten miles to the dances at the Cherry Ridge Grain Hall. We would stay late, laugh, dance, and catch up on the news. The children would play together until they were tired, then curl up in the pile of coats and sleep until we left. When we left we depended on the horse knowing the way home. We would sleep in the back of the wagon until the horse stopped outside the barn. It was great fun.

Father was sixty-eight years old and still in good health. He was often gruff and opinionated, and seemed a bit more distant and temperamental as he got older, but he loved the children and would do anything for them. He refused to slow down. He still lived with us but was only there a few weeks at a time. He would often be fishing in the mountains or hunting in Canada. He still took jobs for the Great Northern. He was a respected consultant on lumber prices and land values. The railroad was constantly looking to buy forestland for firewood, railroad ties, and other uses, and the lands in western Montana, Idaho, and eastern Washington were prime for purchase. Father's job was to get the best price possible, which often involved negotiating and sometimes court cases when an owner challenged the price. Father's stubbornness and refusal to back down from a fight made him the perfect man to represent the railroad. They loved having him on their team because he always got them the best deal possible. Unfortunately, it gave him more opportunity to speculate on the land purchases. He once was a successful speculator, but as he aged he lost more than he profited.

The railroad jobs would frequently take him away for a month or two, but he didn't mind. I think he liked the solitude and freedom to come and go without bothering us. It could be frustrating because he rarely communicated his plans. One day he would be with us on the farm, then the next he would pack up and be gone. We never knew how long he would be gone, and then he would show up at the door. "Job's done," is about all he would say.

One day I asked him about his work and if he ever intended to slow down. "I've got to keep working," he said. "I've got to stay active – it's just the way I am. Besides, I know nothing about farming and we need the money. So quit telling me to slow down."

It was another hot, dry summer and our little irrigation pond could not keep up with the demands of the crops for more and more water. At the annual community feast on the Fourth of July everyone was pessimistic about chances for a good crop. It seemed the whole county was burning up. One day Harry went into Chinook and came back shaking his head with disgust.

"Everyone in town was talking about the drought. The government men say it's the same everywhere in Montana and the Dakotas. The land is crying for water and there doesn't seem to be any relief in sight. The old-timers who have been in Montana since the turn of the century say it's just the way things are out here. They said there are six to eight years of rain, then six to eight years of drought. If they're right, we've got another couple years of no rain." He grimaced at the thought.

"Besides that, the prices of wheat and oats have dropped over twenty cents a bushel. They are down to a buck fifty a bushel. Two years ago we got almost two fifty a bushel. I used to get almost forty or fifty bushels per acre, now I'm getting less than ten bushels. Doesn't look good Mabel."

"We have to keep praying for rain. Not much more we can do." I was trying to stay positive, but it was hard.

"The men in town are mad at the railroad. They are talking about their false advertising to get us all out here. Remember some of those flyers we would see? They all said how wonderful it was in Montana and how anything would grow here."

"Oh, I sure do. Some of them were way too good to be true. They claimed this was the richest farmland in America. And always talking about how much rain Montana got. What a pack of lies."

"You can almost laugh at those now," Harry said. "And the whole 'dry-land farming' system they promoted. I guess it works, but it sure doesn't conserve the water in the soil like they said it would."

Yet we still wrote to Michigan and encouraged sister Hazel and brother Riley to come to Montana. We would get them land and jobs if they came. It would be so nice to have family close and we didn't want to worry Mother and Father Green about our situation.

Harvest time came in August and early September but there wasn't much to take. Most of the wheat had shriveled with the summer heat and drought, and the barley and flax were spotty. Harry returned from Chinook after taking what he could to market with a stoic look on his face.

"Well, guess that's all we're goin' to get this year. Prices are down and the drought has cut our yield to almost nothing. Going to be another tight winter, dear."

I looked at him and smiled. "But it's going to be a happy spring." I paused to get his attention. "I'm pregnant. Probably due in April."

"Really? April? Wonderful. Maybe it will be another boy to keep Charles company."

"Or," I said, "maybe it will be a sister for Harriet. Either way, our little family is growing."

We were poor, but didn't know it. We always said, "We don't have any money, but we're rich in family and friends." The entire community of Cherry Ridge was in the same condition and worked together to help each other. I had a bumper crop of tomatoes – thanks to the water from our pond. Bessie Slonaker grew potatoes and traded a bushel of potatoes for a dozen jars of tomatoes. The Petersons gave radishes and carrots in trade for my tomatoes. The Furchtbars slaughtered a couple pigs and traded smoked pork for vegetables. This had been going on from the beginning, but was even more important as we faced our third drought year in a row.

"Alma Tinker is selling out," Harry exclaimed one day after coming in from the fields. "She's not getting any crops and can't afford her hired hand. Said she is going to get whatever she can for the land and go to her parents' back east."

I wasn't surprised. "She hasn't been too enthusiastic about the land for a couple years. I wasn't even sure she would be able to get her patent. She should get what she can."

Harry agreed. "She's not alone. I've heard of more and more homesteaders leaving their land. Some are selling, some are just leaving. This drought is hurting everybody. There is nothing in the fields. I can't even hire out because there is so little to harvest."

I noticed Harry's tone was changing. "Are we going to have to sell out Harry? Are we in tough shape?"

"I think we're okay for now. Especially if Edmond can help us get through the winter. I know he's going back to Seattle, but maybe he can give us a loan until spring. If we can make it to February, I can sell some livestock. I've got four mares in foal and I can sell the colts in the spring for a decent price." He looked at me and laughed his loving laugh, "Besides, you're in foal yourself. You aren't going anywhere for a while."

It was a mild winter by Montana standards, with only a couple feet of snow and less than a month below-zero temperatures, but being almost six months pregnant made it even more uncomfortable than usual. I couldn't get out, even on the nicest winter days, and was stuck in the house with two small children. Harry did his best to keep me occupied and was inside most of the day after the morning chores and feedings. We played a lot of cards, made up games with the children, and made small repairs to the house. Father sent me some sheet music from Seattle and I practiced on the piano to memorize the new songs.

February 28, 1921, was a cold, crisp winter morning where the air was still and sounds were magnified by the silence of the prairie. I heard an automobile approaching when it was still miles away and was curious what would bring someone out this far at this time of the year. When I looked out the window to see what was going on, Harry came rushing through the doorway.

"Looks like Sheriff Cramer coming this way. I don't have time to explain things, Mabel, but I think he's coming for me."

"What did you do Harry?" was all I could get out.

"It's a long story. Just don't panic or say anything right now. I'll probably have to go with him for tonight, but after I post bail I'll be back and explain it all. I'll be fine."

It wasn't Sheriff Cramer, but his deputy, Ira Holt. When Harry saw who it was he was relieved. "Holt," he yelled when the deputy got out of the car, "How ya been? What brings you out here? I know you aren't looking to come back and work on my threshing crew at this time of year."

When he was younger, Holt had spent some time working with Harry's threshing crew, but he tried to look serious now. "Harry Greene. I'm here to arrest you on a charge of grand larceny for stealing and killing the steer of Martin Rekedal. Are you going to come peacefully?"

"Ha – Rekedal is accusing me of stealing his steer?" said Harry with a confident tone. "Ol' Martin can't keep track of his livestock, so he's accusing me of stealing it? He's crazy. I'll bet the darn steer has wandered away from the barn and Rekedal can't find it. You want me to ride into town with you? Be glad to – I've got nothing to worry about."

"Then you won't mind me looking around your place a bit?" asked the deputy.

"Go right ahead. Mabel and I don't have anything to hide." Harry was doing his best to stay confident and cheerful.

Deputy Holt looked around for some time. After looking in the barn, he came out with a cowhide he found hanging in a stall. "Harry," he said, "this hide has your Z/T brand, but something doesn't look right with the brand. You didn't change the brand did you?"

"Don't know. Maybe I missed one," said Harry. "Coulda been a lousy bit of branding I guess."

"Well, I've got to take this in to the station. We'll let the judge sort it all out." They got in the automobile, with Harry in the back seat, and headed into Chinook.

It was a lonely, tension-filled night. I was sure Harry would be back out to the ranch in the next day or two. I knew he would try to talk his way out of it, but grand larceny was a very serious charge. I had two little children and was over seven months pregnant with the third and couldn't imagine what would happen if he was found guilty and sent to jail. I would have to do everything myself.

He was in jail three days. Two days after his arrest I took Father's automobile and the children and drove to the Blaine County Jail in Chinook. Harry was sitting in his cell with Everett Isbell, who was accused of being Harry's accomplice. They were laughing and telling stories as if they were at dinner enjoying a cup of coffee. When Harry saw me he was surprised and excited, but didn't say much.

"What are you doing here?" was his first, rather silly, question.

"Obviously, I came to visit my husband. Tell me what's happening. How long are you going to be here?"

Harry looked around to make sure the deputy wasn't going to hear. "Don't worry. I'll be home tomorrow night and tell you everything. We are waiting for Judge Ross. He's a good man – I've done some work for him in the past and he's fair. I will plead not guilty tomorrow and he will set bail. I've already wired E. C. for help with the cost of bail. He'll get his money back. I'll tell you everything tomorrow night."

The next night, as the sun was going down, another automobile rumbled across the prairie and delivered my man back home.

"Thank goodness your father has some connections around this county," was the first thing Harry said as he got out of the car and thanked the driver for bringing him out. "The judge set bail at two thousand dollars. It was crazy. E. C. didn't have it, but he called some friends and called the bank and arranged to have the money transferred so I could get out. I owe him."

"So what is this all about?" I asked after Harry passed out hugs and kisses to the children.

"This all started as a prank," Harry said and I knew it was going to be quite a story. "You know old Martin Rekedal. Well, every winter for the last three or four winters he has let some of his livestock wander around free range. He doesn't care, since they usually end up on someone else's ranch mixed in with their livestock and eating their feed. In the spring Rekedal shows up, reclaims his cattle, and doesn't pay a thing to the rancher who fed them all winter. It's a game he plays to get his cattle fed for free.

"Well, one day in January, Everett Isbell and I were out riding the range, checking the fence line and looking for strays when we saw this big steer moseying across the south pasture. We both knew it was Rekedal's from the brand and we both knew it was part of his scheme. We decided to teach him a lesson. We weren't about to feed it all winter, so we brought the steer here, killed it, and butchered it. I meant to take care of the hide before the spring, but hadn't done it yet. I didn't think Rekedal would ask any questions or complain until spring. Surprised he did something now."

Harry's boldness at killing the steer didn't surprise me, but I was upset with his cavalier attitude. He thought it was all a good joke. "How stupid of you. How could you do that without thinking of the consequences? Aren't you worried? Grand larceny is a major charge. If you're found guilty you could be in prison for a long time. I can't raise these youngsters without you. I'm seven months pregnant. This is crazy."

"Now don't get all in a tizzy, Mabel," he said confidently. "First of all, we will say we didn't know it was Rekedal's. I plan to deny whatever he says. It was a stray. There are stray cattle all over this county, everyone knows that."

"But the deputy took the hide. It's proof you had the steer."

Suddenly Harry started laughing and couldn't stop. "That's the best part," and he laughed so much he couldn't finish the sentence. "The hide disappeared between here and Chinook. Seems it somehow fell out of the car while deputy Holt was focused on driving across the prairie trails." And he laughed even more.

"Harry Greene. Did you throw the hide away?" I was stunned at his boldness.

"Well, all I can say is that without the hide, they don't have any evidence to connect the steer to me. It's going to be hard to convict me without any evidence." His smile stretched from ear to ear like it always did whenever he pulled a good stunt on someone. "And you can deny any knowledge of the whole thing. You never saw the hide in the barn or anything. So we're covered."

The trial was set for June. In the meantime, there was lots of work to get done.

Spring came with more news of settlers abandoning their land. It seemed folks were moving out of central Montana

Mary R. #J. in my Baby dress.

Mabel with
Mary Rosemond, 1921

as fast as they had moved in eight earlier. We stuck it out, but it got tougher and tougher. Harry was able to sell the colts, although he lost one little filly at birth in the winter. And Father sent some money from Seattle to keep our heads above water.

In the midst of these tough times Mary Rosemond Green was born on April 24, 1921. I was able to get to the doctor's office in Cherry Ridge for the birth. She came right on time, was a beautiful baby,

and was healthy and active from the start. Harriet was more excited than anyone else. She looked at the baby and squealed, "Mama, now I have a playmate. I can be her big sister."

Spring delivered mild breezes and fields of wildflowers in bloom. It even rained and we all prayed the drought was ending. But the rains were brief, barely enough to moisten the soil and definitely not enough to sink down and restore the dried-up subsoil. Harry cut back the amount of land seeded hoping to get a bigger yield from a more concentrated area. He chose the fields that had been most successful the last few years and closest to the reservoir. He left more to fallow and pasture in hopes of restoring some nutrition and moisture to the land. He spread manure, dug new irrigation ditches, drilled the well deeper, moved crops around, and anything else he could think of to promote growth.

We could not afford a hired hand, and I could not help as much as I had in the past with three youngsters, so Harry was forced to work the fields himself. He still had his tractor but was so busy he was unable to do as much hiring out as he had in years past, so we didn't have any extra cash. When he did get a job, it was further away and often required him to be away for up to a week to get the job done. He was always in the field, either our own or someone else's, so when he came home he was exhausted.

Harriet became my primary helper. She was not yet five years old but became more responsible and loved caring for baby Rosemond. She would rock her, watch her sleep, and tell me if the baby needed anything. Charles, meanwhile, was walking and talking and playing in the yard most of the day. He was non-stop motion, would wander a bit, and often test my rules. But all three children were even tempered and enjoyed themselves.

Harry's trial was set to begin on June thirteenth. Everett Isbell chose to have a separate trial. Harry hired his friend, E. J. McCabe, as his defense attorney and elected to have a jury trial. I left the children with Bessie and attended the trial. I was told I might need to testify for the defense about what I knew about the charges – which I could easily do, since I knew nothing about the events. It was frightening to hear the bailiff charge Harry "did willfully, unlawfully, and feloniously steal, take, and carry away one steer, the personal property of one Martin Rekedal." I still wasn't sure he could talk his way out of this mess.

The prosecutor only called two witnesses – Mr. Rekedal and his neighbor Mr. Fleming – to testify the steer was Rekedal's, was missing, and was last seen heading toward our land. Mr. McCabe, on the other hand, had over twenty people from the prairie community – including E.C. and me – ready to testify about stray, unbranded cattle wandering through everyone's pasture, and how difficult it was to keep track of whose cattle was on your land. Harry testified himself, stating he thought the steer was a stray, did not see any brand, and had no knowledge Rekedal was missing the steer. The final deciding factor, though, was the absence of any evidence. The hide could not be produced so there was no evidence to connect the missing steer to Harry.

The jury was out for only one hour before they returned with a "not guilty" verdict. Harry was free. His fast talk and bluster had served him well one more time. He was a lucky man.

That night, we had a party at the ranch. Everyone who had testified in Harry's defense was invited over for a big beef roast. People came from miles around and ate and drank. The liquor, of course, was brought from Canada since Prohibition was still in effect. The men laughed and laughed about how Harry had taught Ol' Man Rekedal a lesson and how he would keep track of his livestock in the future. Everyone knew it was a temporary victory and he would probably let his livestock wander in the future, but it was a good cause for celebration.

Bessabel

The drought continued through the rest of 1921 and into 1922 with little letup in the heat. There had not been significant moisture for over four years. By mid summer 1922 it was obvious it would be another tough year. The rivers were down and the underground water table was shrinking rapidly. Everyone had to drill deeper wells. The fields were brown with shriveled grains. Father even reported the hunting was the worst he had seen since many of the animals had moved to higher, lusher locations.

Harry was forced to sell ten horses to bring in some money and cut the size of his herd. He did have strong horses, which brought in good money, but he was disappointed to have to sell them and found it a frustrating experience.

By September 1922 Harry was the most depressed I had ever seen him. He still joked and kept a smile on his face, but I could tell he was down. It affected both of us. Even our letters were less optimistic, and, for the first time, we discouraged family from coming to Montana.

"I think you made the right decision not moving here last year," Harry wrote to his brother, Frank, in the fall. "If you did come, I'm sure you could find a farm for almost no money since so many settlers are giving up and moving back east. It's been so dry most folks have no crops to bring in." And to another friend back in Michigan he wrote, "I'd suggest you stay right there at least until next spring. If the drought breaks you might think of coming out, but it's hard to tell."

I tried not to dwell on our poverty and keep my letters upbeat, but sometimes it proved impossible. In one letter to Hazel I admitted, "I'm absolutely out of clothes. Haven't had a suit since I was married and even my trousseau underclothes are worn out now. I need so little out on the ranch that I've had almost nothing – no I don't go naked." Still, Harry and I constantly reminded each other we were rich with love and family.

In the fall Harriet started school at the little one-room schoolhouse. There were eight other children at the school, even with families moving out. She would ride her horse, Tootsie, to school in the morning, then the horse would find its way back to the farm. She loved school and learned quickly. Most of all she enjoyed being with the other children from the surrounding farms. I missed her help and Charles missed having her to play with, but it was good to watch her grow and learn. I had been teaching her letters and numbers at home, but it was exciting to see her progress at the school.

Our little community stayed together and supported each other. Harry and I didn't travel back to Michigan in the winter and rarely went farther than Chinook when we went anywhere. Father was gone with railroad contracts and Harry hired out on fields whenever he could. He tried to get a construction job in Chinook during the winter months, but there were so many men looking for jobs in town he was never successful in finding anything worthwhile.

I became pregnant in the fall of 1922, due in May 1923. As expected, life was even more uncomfortable in the winter.

But we loved our children and both wanted a big family, so the prospect of another mouth to feed never bothered us. Although times were tough, we still loved living on the prairie and being a family.

In April 1923 Father returned from his winter stay in Seattle. He was full of stories and was as dominating as ever. Everything seemed normal. He played with the children and loved taking them for rides across the prairie. It gave us more time to work in the fields.

Spring always came with a sense of hope and Harry resumed his hard work. He successfully extended his loan with the bank and felt confident we would finally get a wet season to help our crops. But he wasn't himself. He was lackadaisical and had no energy. He would come home earlier than normal and sleep more. Worse, he started having fever and intestinal problems. He could not keep food down and had diarrhea. He became dehydrated. Finally, he consented to calling Dr. O'Malley in Chinook.

When the doctor arrived Harry couldn't get out of bed, had labored breathing, and a fever of 105 degrees. The doctor looked at him briefly, then turned to me and said, "Harry's Catholic, isn't he?"

"Yes, he is. Why do you ask?" I was worried by the tone of his voice.

"I think you had better get a priest out here. He may need to give last rites."

"No. Harry can't die." I was panicked at the thought. It really hadn't crossed my mind.

The doctor was examining Harry when Father entered the room. The doctor asked, "Do you know if anyone has been around some contagious disease like typhoid or diphtheria?"

Father, in his matter-of-fact way, chirped in, "Well sure. I was in Seattle all winter and typhoid is pretty common there. I probably had contact with the germ, but I'm not sick, so it couldn't be me."

"Papa," I screamed. "Why didn't you tell us? You are carrying the germ here to the prairie. Nobody here has been exposed. You could kill us all." I was furious at his stupidity. "Get out of here before you infect the children. Go get a priest for Harry and clean up. You are sleeping in the barn until this is all over." He looked at me to respond, then, seeing how angry I was, shook his head and left.

Harry was going in and out of consciousness with the delirium of the fever. We thought we had lost him a couple times before the priest arrived. When he came, the priest took one look at Harry and started giving him last rites. But Harry rallied and broke the fever. We thought he would pull through. Then he relapsed and went back into the delirium. He fought the fever and dehydration for over a week. The priest returned one other time and again gave the last rites in case Harry died after he left. All this time, Bessie and Elmer Slonaker were with us providing food and care for the children. Bessie's main concern was my health, since I was close to my delivery date.

While Harry was fighting for his life, I went into labor early. The stress of caring for Harry had caused me to start labor pains. Bessie had been at our house every day since Harry had taken ill and was watching over both of us. She insisted I go into Chinook to have the baby. Elmer drove me into town while she watched Harry.

On May 18, 1923, I delivered another lovely baby girl. Harry and I had not discussed names and I didn't want to name her until he recovered and could help me decide. Father – who had since been checked out and determined to be germ free – and Elmer Slonaker brought me word Harry was recovering and would be healthy enough to visit in a few days. So I waited in the hospital without naming my little girl.

My physician, Dr. O'Malley, became impatient and wanted to get the birth certificate signed, so he decided to put "Mabel Greene" as the baby's name. When Harry finally got to the hospital two days later it caused considerable confusion, especially since Harry had the perfect name for the little girl.

"Mabel," he said with love in his voice, "while I was in and out of consciousness I knew you and Bessie were there for me, and I knew I was getting the best care possible. I wasn't able to talk, but I heard your voices. And when I heard we had a little girl, I immediately knew what we were going to name her."

I was amazed he could do all that while struggling for his life. "What did you decide on?"

"I knew it had to be something to honor the two most important women in my life. We will name her Bessabel – from Bessie and Mabel."

"I love it," I exclaimed. "We can call her Becky, but her name will be Bessabel. Yes – perfect."

And that's how our little family grew in the midst of another dry, terrible year with disease, a birth, and a lot of love.

Drought and Hard Times

1924 was the fifth year of drought on the High Plains. Everywhere – the Dakotas, Nebraska, Colorado, Wyoming, and further south all the way to Texas – had the same problem: no water. It was destroying the idyllic prairie community we had developed. The southern Plains around Oklahoma, eastern Colorado, and the Texas Panhandle were being engulfed with massive dust storms that suffocated the meager crops. Everywhere settlers were abandoning their farms and looking for jobs.

"Well, Roy Croft is leaving," said Harry one day after coming back from a visit to our neighbors. "The bank is foreclosing on his loan. He has nothing left."

I shook my head in disbelief. "I thought Roy was doing okay. He's the fourth to leave in the last year. Be honest with me – how are we doing? Are we going to have to join them?"

Harry looked downcast. "Not yet, but it's getting real tough. I'm going to have to sell more horses and cattle before winter sets in for us to make it through. The bank keeps telling me I've got to make some payments or they will foreclose on us. Thankfully your father is contributing enough to keep us solvent. But if I can't get a decent crop next year ..." He didn't finish the sentence. I knew what he was thinking.

We struggled all summer. Harry hunted more and we ate more prairie chicken, duck, and antelope than ever before. Wood and coal were too expensive so we sent the children out on the prairie to pick up cow chips, which we burned exclusively. Since the well was dry we hauled water from the reservoir twice a day. Every egg and every pail of milk was treasured and handled with great care. I almost ran out of canned vegetables in the root cellar. The sun kept bearing down on us and it did not rain enough to put ripples in the water barrel.

Harriet, Rosemond, Becky
& Charles on Sam

The children were our saving grace and kept both of us working hard to provide for them. I called them my "Chinook Coyotes" because, on any given day, they could be as cute, or as mischievous, as a High Plains coyote. Harriet and Charles were old enough to help gather eggs and feed the livestock. Charles always made doing the chores a contest, trying to collect more eggs or get more feed than Harriet. She, in turn, usually let him win and would laugh when he jumped around and yelled how he had beaten his sister. Rosemond and Bessabel were too young to help, but they watched me in the house and talked to me throughout the day. Harriet would watch her sisters and help with the feeding and care of the baby.

Father was now seventy-one years old and finally slowing down. He stayed at the ranch more than in years past. He was handy with machinery and could help Harry with the tractor and other farm equipment. He bought a truck and drove it all over the prairie looking for new hunting and fishing spots. He loved to take four-year-old Charles on drives and talk to him about all sorts of outdoors adventures. Charles had his own pony and had no fear of anything, so Father would often go horseback riding with him. He would beg Father to ride or play whenever he could.

Our crops continued to struggle. Much of the wheat we planted in the fall barely came up and what did was shriveled up by July. The flax and barley, which had been more drought-resistant in past years, lasted to early August before they too shriveled up. Everyone was in the same situation. Harry couldn't get any work hiring out his tractor since most farmers in the area had cut back on the amount of land tilled. He was good with horses and made some extra cash working as a wrangler and breaking wild horses for other ranchers in the area, but it wasn't a steady income.

In late October it rained for two days. It was much too late for this year's crop, but it gave everyone hope for the future. When we got to church all the men were talking about next year.

"This will be the start of a wet season, I'm sure," Elmer Slonaker said.

"Yep, if we can get a little more rain, and then a decent snow cover this winter, we'll be fine by May," said Pete Peterson.

"I sure hope so," said Harry, still not sounding totally convinced. "I'm pretty disgusted with this drought. Something's gotta give or we'll all be heading back east. I'm going to

233

try one more crop of winter wheat and see what I've got next year. I think I can get enough out of the bank to get my seed in, but they are being pretty tight with money."

Elmer laughed. "If anyone can talk them outta their money, it's you Harry. You've got the gift."

Harry smiled and patted Elmer on the back. "Might be true there, Elmer, but I think I'm going to go to church and say a little prayer, just in case."

Everyone was praying for rain. When it rained – even a little – we all got excited. We didn't need much to get our hopes up for the future.

Harry got the loan, with a high interest rate and a short pay-back time, and went to Canada again to get seed. He planted a hundred acres of winter wheat, plowed and disced another two hundred in preparation for the spring, then sat back and watched the weather. It was a wetter autumn than the last few years. Not a record, by any means, but wet enough to raise the level in the reservoir. Then the snows came. Dry, fluffy snow, and enough to provide insulation for the seeds.

It was a cold, windy winter. Father went to Seattle for his winter stay, but with four youngsters it got a bit close in the house. Harry took care of the livestock and worked in the barn repairing and maintaining his equipment. When the weather eased up he would go hunting with Elmer Slonaker. They would always return with some sort of fresh meat, even if it was only a few prairie chickens or geese from the pond. Most of the time though, he would come back with a mule deer to provide us with meat for a couple weeks.

Harriet and Charles were in school. Each morning they would ride through the snow to the little building down the road. It wasn't too far, and they could get there in about twenty minutes, so the weather was rarely a problem. If it was too cold or if a winter storm came up, they would stay home and I would give them a lesson. Rosemond was only three, but she wanted to do what her sister and brother were doing, so I gave her lessons on numbers and some simple reading. She picked it up quickly. I wanted to make sure my children got the best education possible and would go out of my way to ensure they completed their lessons correctly.

The spring of 1925 came with more hopeful signs than the last few years. The grasses seemed greener and the wild-flowers more abundant. Our wheat started peeking up in the fields and Harry put in flax and barley as soon as the fields were workable. I put in my vegetable garden. The livestock even seemed to enjoy a better than average spring. Three calves and four colts were born and the hens had more chicks than in years past. Things were looking up.

A spring thunderstorm approached from the southwest. The clouds piled high, darkened, and threatened the entire county. Harry was concerned about hail, but the storm came with great fanfare of terrible loud thunder, a sky full of light-ning, a steady rain, but no hail. As it passed Harry breathed easier, looked at the sky and said, "That's what we needed, a good long rain. Maybe this year will be better."

A week later we had to face reality. The whole family squeezed into Father's auto and went into Chinook for the day. I took the children and shopped for groceries and sup-plies to get us through the summer. Harry went to the bank to discuss our debt and try to extend the loan. We needed the money to be able to buy seed and pay off the tractor and farm equipment.

Harry walked out of the bank with the frustrated look that told me something was wrong.

"Trouble?" was all I asked.

Harry shook his head. "I couldn't get Ol' Man Harbolt to extend my loan. He has extended it twice already but says he can't do any more. Can you believe it? He tells me the bank doesn't have enough money to extend the loan. Said there are too many ranchers in the area in the same boat and they can't grant any more extensions. What the Hell is a bank for if not to give us a loan? They said they're short of money. That made me laugh."

I could tell he was angry and it wasn't going to do any good to get more heated, so I tried to calm him down a bit. "So? The crops are coming in well. It looks like it will be a good year. Can't we make a payment on the loan when our crops come in?"

"That's what's so frustrating," he said. "We're finally having a good year and it's going to take everything we have to make a small dent in our loan. We will need a record yield. We will need more than we got back in 1917 when we had our biggest yield yet. I've got to relook at the numbers. We might not be able to pay off the loan, pay taxes, and feed the family – and my first priority is to feed the family. To Hell with the bank and the taxes."

Father wasn't any help. He only succeeded in getting Harry riled up even more. "Well, I can't believe it either. Damned Harbolt only thinks of himself. They don't think about us out here on the farms and ranches. All they want is their money. I think Harbolt would be happy to drive us off the land. Then he can buy it up himself. The SOB wants to control the whole county." We could no longer expect Father to help since he was being slowly phased out as an employee of the Great Northern. They hadn't asked him to work in over six months and he was living with us full time on the ranch. He was costing us money, but we didn't mind. He had made plenty of contributions to the ranch and the family through the years.

In late May 1925 I added one more complication to our situation. "Harry, dear, I'm pregnant again. I've missed my time of the month. By my calculations I will be due in late January or early February."

"Well, it doesn't change much moneywise," said Harry. "I guess it only means you won't be doing much in the fields this fall. That's okay. By then we will know if we can stay here or will have to go."

He hadn't said this before and he caught me off guard. "What do you mean, if we can stay here? I thought the crops were coming in well."

"Oh, they are. Could be our best crop in many years, but I don't think it will satisfy the bank. Grain prices aren't too great and unless they go up considerably we won't be getting what we should for our harvest. If I can't get some jobs threshing and working fields we won't make it."

"What will we do? Are you saying they're going to take our land? We've done too much, gone through too many trials and tribulations. They can't simply take it away." I started tearing up, but the children were there and I didn't want to upset them.

"Don't panic Mabel. We'll work something out. I think I can probably get enough to keep them at bay for a little while. Maybe we should go back to Michigan until we can get some money built up. Remember the letter I got last month from Mother and Father Green?"

"Yes. They wanted us to come home for Christmas again. I wrote them back and said I didn't see how we could afford it. Was there something I missed?"

"Remember they talked about Uncle Hal in Chicago? He's got lots of money and is helping build more railroads in the Chicago area. If I go to work for him I can get enough money to pay off the bank and back taxes, and get this place back on its feet."

We worked hard that summer. We had more rain and the crops grew well. I helped out as much as possible, but the children, and my pregnancy, kept me from doing too much. Father wanted to hire a laborer, but it would take money we needed to pay down the debt. Harry worked himself into a frenzy. He worked our fields, then went out on his tractor and hired out to a few other ranchers. He worked breaking horses and doing odd construction jobs. He was busy every day from before dawn to after dark. He had to be exhausted, but he never complained. As a matter of fact, most of the time he bragged about his ability to work longer, harder hours than the average man.

"Can't stop me now," he'd brag. "They can't hold me down. I'm a bundle of energy. I know I'm probably scaring you, Mabel, but I've got to keep going so I don't think about our debt."

The harvest was in by the end of September and we had done better than previous years. We had 350 bushels of wheat, 100 of barley, and 240 of flax. But prices were down everywhere, even in Canada. Harry sold more, but got less than ever. It seemed so unfair.

"We've got enough to keep the bank off our back for another year," he said one morning after working on the numbers late the night before. But I don't think we've got enough to pay the taxes and we won't have any savings at all. I've made a decision. You might not like it, but I think it's the only way we can get out of this trap between the bank and the taxes."

"I may not like it, but if you've thought it all through, then it's okay. What's your plan?"

"If I sell off the livestock and my farm equipment, we will have enough money to go to Michigan this winter. I'll go work with Uncle Hal long enough to build up our savings. Maybe six or eight months. Then we will come back to the ranch with some money in our pockets. We should be able to return next year by August or September."

"Oh Harry, it all sounds so desperate. Can't we get someone to watch the livestock? If you sell the farm equipment will you be able to get more? Have you written anyone back home to see if it will work with them?"

"Mother Green has already written back. We would be welcome and could live with them. We will make more money selling the livestock than keeping them. We will buy more when we come back. I'm starting to think it's the best option. If we stay here through the winter there won't be any work and we will be in the same money crunch next year. If we move now we can get a small nest egg built up and won't have to scrimp and save all the time. Maybe then I can buy you some of those nice things you've always wanted."

I looked at him with a smile. "I don't care about anything other than to be with you and the children. If you think it's the best plan, then I agree."

To Michigan: 1925

It was time to do something drastic. We had been fighting the drought, the land, and the bank for twelve years and had not gotten even an inch ahead of the margin. We had plenty of land, but the land had let us down and was not producing the yields we hoped for. We had much more money invested in the land than we would ever get selling out. The price of land had dropped out of sight with the drought years. Harry was an accomplished farmer, horseman, wrangler, and carpenter, but all his hard work had been for naught. We had tried farming, ranching, and even renting out land, but – since everyone in the area was in the same predicament – we had nothing to show for it. It was time to try a different approach.

Harry and Mabel with Harriet, Rosemond, Charles, and Bessabel, 1925

Harry sold his tractor, plow, disc, and thresher. He

sold the horses and cattle. He got a good price on all of it and saved every penny for the trip east. We gave our chickens and goats to our neighbors. The only things Harry would not sell were the children's ponies. He asked the Slonakers to take care of them. Harriet and Charles had their own ponies. Rosemond and Bessabel weren't old enough yet to have their own, but he kept one very gentle mare for them when we returned.

And we would return. Harry promised me, and anyone else who asked. We would be back on the ranch before the winter of 1926. He had it all figured out. A solid spring and-summer of working for Uncle Hal in the railyards of Chicago, living with Hal, and saving every dime he earned, would give him a big enough bankroll to return by the autumn harvest.

In October the Cherry Ridge community gave us a grand sendoff. Bessie Slonaker hosted the gathering. There were ten different families all gathered around eating at tables

The Greens and Slonakers, Late 1925

set up in their front yard. I brought my Kodak Brownie camera and took plenty of pictures. My favorites were the pictures of the children. One shows my four children and the Slonaker children all together on the back of our horse, Sam. Another favorite is of the two families – Greens and Slonakers – standing in waist high grass. It is a classic prairie land pose. There were plenty of hugs and kisses, lots of stories about the times on the prairie, and love passed all around. We cried and laughed and made promises to return. It was a wonderful party and sendoff, but somehow I knew in my heart it would never be the same. I cried most of the night after we got home.

Father, meanwhile, was concerned. Not about us of course, but about his own future. He didn't want to go to Michigan with us. He would go to Seattle for the winter, but did not know what he would do in the spring. If he came back to Chinook or Havre he would probably be pressured to pay the back taxes. If he came to Michigan he was sure he would not find a place to live, since the Greens' invitation indicated there would not be room for him. He became grouchy and irritable as we got closer and closer to our departure. We decided it was best to let the decision wait until next spring after we were settled in Michigan.

I was anxious to leave since I was pregnant and getting bigger every day. But Harry had to finish up business around the ranch. He went to the bank and paid as much as he could to decrease the debt and assure them he was still a good risk. He did not tell them of our plan to take a year off, since he was afraid they might try to foreclose and take the land while we were gone. He buttoned up the house, barn, and granary for the coming winter and the next season of storms. It was early December before everything was prepared. We had promised the Greens we would be in Michigan for Christmas, so it was time to go.

Father took us to the Chinook train depot early in the morning on December 15, 1925. We took the Great Northern east to St. Paul, then to Chicago, and finally Jackson. All our possessions were stuffed into two trunks and a beautiful cedar chest Father had made me years earlier. Everything else was either sold or left behind. As the train pulled out of the station I could hear Mother's words. "Don't look back – look to the future." And, "You can't undo the past, stay positive about life and your loved ones." Finally, she would always say, "Live your life to the fullest. Face the challenges and overcome them." I knew it would take hard work to keep all those things in my head in the near future.

It took three long days on the train to get to Jackson. I was seven months pregnant and trying to control four young children. We were all squeezed into a small Pullman sleeping car where I tried to keep everyone happy and rested. It didn't work. There was lots of shouting, crying, and little sleep. We stopped at depots for meals, but those were never long enough to cut into Charles' endless energy supply. We were a tired, grouchy family when we finally reached the station. But by the time brother Riley brought us to the Green residence in Parma we had settled down and made ourselves presentable guests.

Harry made one small concession to move back home. He removed the "e" from the end of "Greene" at his father's insistence. It was a simple thing done to keep his parents happy.

We had a wonderful Christmas. The entire Green family was there and we told endless stories of life on our Montana ranch. The children played with their cousins and Harry and I talked about our immediate plans. We decided to rent a small house near Mother and Father Green while Harry working in Chicago.

I enrolled the children into the local school as quickly as possible. It was a one-room school, so Harriet and Charles could work together. Rosemond was old enough for kindergarten, but caught a nasty cold on the trip east, which turned into pneumonia. She was much too sick to go to school, so I schooled her at home on her letters and numbers. She caught on quickly and always seemed jealous of the older children going to school.

Before he left for Chicago Harry delivered a special surprise for Harriet. She had been missing her pony, Tootsie, so Harry had the horse shipped east. The horse arrived shortly before Harry's departure, so he didn't have much time to get Tootsie adjusted to the Midwest forests. Tootsie had never seen so many trees and would shy away and skitter around whenever there was a large grove. Harry tried to break her of her fears, but he could not stay long enough to completely solve the problem. He told Harriet she would have to be very careful where she rode Tootsie and promised he would work with the horse on his next trip home. Unfortunately, Tootsie never overcame her fear of trees and eventually she had to be put down.

As spring approached I started getting comfortable in my surroundings. Spring in southern Michigan was much different than in Montana. I had forgotten how beautiful a forest was when the trees had the light green freshness of early leaves. When the dogwood and redbud trees bloomed they provided a world of color I hadn't seen in years. The lilacs in Mother Green's yard were a brilliant purple with a wonderful scent. Everything was green and fresh. The rivers and streams were full of bubbling, fresh, clear water. The spring rains and storms were wildly refreshing. The air was clear and the winds gently blew across the farm fields. In contrast I remembered the cold night air, the stubble of grains peaking through the soil, and the constant dusty winds blowing across the plains for miles without anything to deflect them. I still loved Montana and the prairie, but I was starting to appreciate Michigan springs.

Uncle Hal was optimistic he would have a good paying job for Harry. He even believed Harry would fall in love with Chicago and want to move the family to the big city. Harry was anxious to get to work and excited about the job but promised me there was no way he would want to stay in Chicago.

"I'm a country boy at heart, Mabel," he assured me. "Don't worry, I'll miss the wide open spaces too much to ever settle down in a city like Chicago. Havre was too big for my taste. Chicago will be work, that's all – no pleasure."

He stayed until the baby was born. On February 19, 1926, Robert Edmond Green was born in Jackson, Michigan. Harry was excited and proud to have another son. I looked at him and could read his mind.

"No, we aren't having any more. I'm thirty-six and you are thirty-seven. I'm not sure it could happen even if we wanted it to." We both laughed at the thought.

Harry looked over lovingly and said, "I'm fine with five. It's a nice number. Besides, I've got two big boys now to show all the things they need to know in life. I'll teach them to hunt and fish and work the fields. They will be first-class boys in no time. You have three lovely little girls to spoil and teach how to be ladies. What more could we ask for?"

A few weeks later, we were settled into our rental and Harry was ready to get to work in Chicago. Halbert Riley – Uncle Hal – was Mother Green's nephew and part owner of a company known as Clapp, Riley, and Hall Equipment that delivered crushed rock and sand aggregate to railroad construction sites. Hal had promised Harry a supervisory position doing construction at the railyards. Harry had been doing odd jobs around his parents' farm but was bored with those projects. He was looking for something more challenging where he could make more money.

"Hal says I can make over ten bucks a day if I play my cards right. Not sure what I'll have to do, but I'm ready to go. I can't wait to get my first big paycheck."

I was worried about Harry in the big city and the possibilities for trouble. "You will be careful right? Chicago has a bad reputation. Stay out of those speakeasies. I know you like an occasional drink, but let Hal get it for you. You don't want to get a Prohibition charge against you. Keep track of your money and don't be wasting it on crazy things. Don't start getting boisterous and overconfident."

Harry laughed the self-assured, confident laugh of his. "Don't lecture me. You don't need to worry. I'll be doing construction and Hal said there would be plenty of overtime. Come on now – can you think of a construction job I can't do? I've been building things and repairing things my whole life. This will be a piece of cake."

I choked back tears as I looked at Harry. "It's not the construction or the big city I'm worried about. I can't fathom the thought of you being gone and so far away from me. Even when you were gone for only two or three days in Montana I missed you terribly. I love you too much. I know we have to do this, but I'm going to miss you. And the children will not know what to do without you."

"Mabel, you know I love you and the children and I wouldn't do this if it wasn't absolutely necessary. It won't be for too long. I'll be back sooner than you think with enough money to get back to the ranch and make a go of it. We can put up with the separation for a couple months. I'll write, I promise." With that he scooped me up in his big hands and gave a long, hard kiss I will never forget.

Harry left for Chicago on June tenth. He kissed us all and climbed aboard the train to Chicago with a promise to return soon. His first letter arrived a week later.

> *Just wanted to let you know I made it to Chicago. Uncle Hal's driver picked me up at Union Station and gave me a drive through Chicago on the way to Willamette, where Hal lives. What a huge, bustling place. I can see why many would find it exciting, but all I see are people, buildings, and pavement. It is chaos. I'm staying at Uncle Hal's place. It is huge – bigger than anything in Montana I'm sure. He has over a dozen servants running around doing things you and I did every-day like cooking, cleaning, gardening. All that stuff. I'm sure I won't get used to having someone come in and make my bed or clean my room. But Hal got me a good job with the railroad. I'm the foreman on a work crew. Not sure what that means, but tomorrow is my first day, so I'll find out soon enough. I've only been gone for a couple days, but I already miss you. Can't wait to get back to see you and our Chinook Coyotes.*

He usually wrote a letter every two or three days, usually mundane things about his job or life at Uncle Hal's mansion. His work crew was a group of Mexican workers who did maintenance on the rail lines in South Chicago. Harry didn't speak any Spanish, so he had to have a translator with him all the time. He picked up bits of the language though and he quickly became friends with the workers. He wasn't afraid to dig in and help out with the dirty work, and, even though they didn't understand everything, they seemed to love his stories of Montana and the songs he would sing as they were working. As he wrote in one letter, "there are plenty of laughs for us all, even though we don't really know what we are laughing about."

He also wrote about the dangers of the railyard. It seemed every letter had a story of someone getting injured on the job, crushed by rail cars, falling, getting burned by sparks and steam, and even killed. Every letter I wrote contained entire paragraphs about safety and begged him to be careful and he always replied "don't worry" and told me how careful he was being. But I knew he was too much of a daredevil and too adventurous to stay back and watch others do the dangerous jobs. I was sure he was right in the middle of it all.

It wasn't all work. Uncle Hal liked to go to the racetrack and Harry's love of horses made the races a natural bonding point for the two of them. Harry's knowledge of horses and ability to see a fast horse in the paddock before a race made them quite successful. I reminded Harry to save his money and not lose it at the track and he replied by telling me about their winnings, but I was worried he might not be saving enough to get us back to Montana as promised.

In June Father completed his winter sojourn in Seattle and unexpectedly showed up at my door in Parma. This was typical of him as he aged. He wouldn't write or give any warning. He expected his only family to take care of him. As he frequently said, "I don't have a wife or any other relatives to care for me. I thought my only daughter would want to take care of her old man." And, of course, I did. He could be a bother and a grouch, but he was my father and I could never turn him away. He made the small area we called a den into a bedroom and was quite comfortable.

Father and Mother Green were good grandparents and loved the children. We went to their farm almost every day. Our relationship was cordial and friendly, but not especially close. Mother Green was, without question, the dominant figure in the family. She was not shy about telling me what I should do and how I should raise my children. After making my own decisions for years on the ranch, I found it a bit annoying. Once, when I mentioned to Harry how much his mother was intruding on my life, he responded with a sarcastic comment of, "Now you know why I left home and went to Montana."

In particular, she always brought up religion. She wanted the children baptized into the Catholic Church, but we resisted. Religion wasn't important to us and Harry had said, even before we left Montana, he would resist his mother's efforts to convert the children. We would visit, talk, laugh, and worry about Harry together, but we never became close confidantes.

Edmond didn't get along with the Greens at all. He was too stubborn and set in his ways and he wasn't going to change for them. Besides, the old religious differences between Catholics and Episcopalians always seemed to come between them. Whenever there was a gathering of the Green family, Father always found an excuse to be absent. He would go hunting or fishing or pretend to be sick. The Greens, for their part, never went out of their way to befriend Father and rarely brought him up in conversation. All in all, it made for some awkward situations.

The summer was a busy time for Harry. He was working as a superintendent for the company of Clapp, Riley, and Hall, who had a huge contract to deliver aggregate rocks and sand throughout the greater Chicago area. It was a good paying job and promised to bring in plenty of money. His letters became less frequent, but when I did get one he talked about how much he was working. One letter summed up his feelings:

> *I'm on the job from dawn until sunset with only Sundays off. I leave Uncle Hal's at five in the morning and don't get back until about ten at night. Then I turn around and do it again the next day. It's driving me crazy. I don't mind the work, but it's the constant day-to-day repetition I don't like. Give me the schedule on the ranch where I can do something different every day, where nature determines what I do and how fast I do it and not some boss with a time schedule. I'll tell you this, Mabel – you don't have to worry about me falling in love with this big city like Hal said. I can't wait to get back to the ranch. If I can save my money, we should be back in Chinook in time for the Thanksgiving feast. I miss you and the children.*
> *All my Love, Red*

My letters always told him how much the children missed him and how much I loved him. The young children all wanted to draw pictures on the letters while Harriet and

Charles would add little stories of school at the bottom of my letters. I always told him to be careful. We all missed him and couldn't wait to get back together again and head back to Montana.

My World Turned Upside Down

On July Fourth, 1926, we all went to the Parma Independence Day picnic, but the children and I left early, much to their chagrin since the children wanted to stay longer. Everyone kept asking about Harry. I hadn't heard from him in days and I was worried. The constant questions wore me out.

July seventh was another hot, humid day. At sunset we could see big thunderclouds forming to the west and coming right at us. Just as I was putting the children to bed, there were huge cracks of thunder and bolts of lightning, followed by a hard rain. We huddled together and I told a bedtime story the little ones liked, then put everyone to bed. Rosemond was still scared, so I let her sleep with me.

About two o'clock in the morning there was a loud knock on the door. I didn't want to open it until Harry's brother said, "It's Tom, open up." I knew. I opened the door, looked at Mother Green's brother, Tom, and started to cry. "It's Harry isn't it? What's happened?" I felt like I was going to faint.

Tom stood there for a minute. He didn't really have to say anything – I knew Harry was dead. Finally, Tom said, "We just got a telegram from Hal. Harry was killed in an accident at the railyard. No details – those will come later."

I sat down and cried hysterically. The children gathered around and tried to understand. Harriet, being the oldest, understood immediately. She told the younger children, "Daddy's not coming home. He's dead." Then she started crying. I think Charles was lost in it all. He knew, but didn't want to accept it. The younger children cried because I was crying. They really didn't understand.

For the second time in my life I had lost by best friend, my comrade, my guide through life. He had been my stabilizer and protector. He had saved me when I was at my lowest point. He led the community and the family. He made all the important decisions and I trusted him totally. And he was gone. Once more I was alone.

I don't remember the next few days. Father and Mother Green came over and tried to comfort me, but they were too

Harry Green – Date unknown

upset themselves to be much help. Harry's sisters, Hazel and Ila, came to watch the children. Papa was no help at all. He had become very close to Harry through the years on the prairie. He left the house and walked through the woods. He wouldn't talk to me, or anyone else. He was as upset as I was. I couldn't sleep. I couldn't eat. I couldn't even talk to anyone without breaking down in tears. I

253

was a total wreck.

He had only been on the job for two weeks, but of course he was doing much of the work himself. There were conflicting stories of what happened. The first story said Harry was killed in an accident in the railyards. He was apparently working under a rail car trying to release something that had jammed up when the hopper opened and dumped the entire load of crushed rock on him. Something about the scenario seemed strange – like why and how did the hopper open – but that's what we kept hearing. Much later I received the official death certificate from Cook County, Illinois. It stated that Harry died from "shock and injuries caused by being caught and crushed while in the act of unloading sand." However, when Uncle Hal came for the funeral, he told the *Jackson Citizen Patriot* Harry fell off scaffolding at a construction site. That was simpler and easier to explain so it was what the paper printed in the obituary. I didn't care. All I knew was Harry was dead. At the time how and why didn't seem to matter. He was only thirty-eight.

I was in shock and numb to everything around me. Uncle Hal took care of the funeral arrangements. He had the body shipped directly to the undertaker and took care of all costs. On July eleventh a limousine pulled up in front of our little place and picked up me and the five children. While I grieved in the front seat the children fought over who had the best seat in the car. They really didn't comprehend what was going on.

I remember very little of the funeral. It was all a blur. The funeral was a quiet service in Jackson, then the body was taken to Hanover for burial. Hal insisted the casket remain closed. He said no one would want to see Harry the way he was after the accident and I was too upset to say differently.

Looking back, I've always regretted not seeing him one more time. Harry's sister, Rita, did get a lock of his beautiful red hair from the funeral director. When I saw it I started crying remembering his beautiful, thick head of hair.

Three days after the funeral Father and Mother Green came to my house. We had not spoken much in the last week other than lamenting Harry's loss and discussing the funeral. It was obvious they came for a reason. When they came in all they said was, "We have to talk."

"Of course," I said. "Sit down and I'll make a pot of tea."

Mother Green quickly said, "No tea. Thank you. We want to talk about the children. Do you have any idea what you are going to do now?"

I told myself to stay calm and rational. "I haven't had much time to think about it. This has been very upsetting. According to Uncle Hal, I am entitled to some insurance money. I think he said it would be about twenty-five hundred dollars. That's a lot of money."

"But you can't live on that forever," exclaimed Mother Green. "What are you going to do for money?"

"I don't know yet. Maybe I'll go back to Montana and the ranch. I can hire some workers and we can make a go of it again. I could rent out the land."

"It's almost the end of July, Mabel," said Father Green. "You can't get out there in time to put in any crop or do anything until next spring. You would be stuck out there with all five children."

I couldn't stay calm any longer. I lost it and started crying. "What do you think I should do? Harry was everything. He was my entire life. I'm thirty-six with five children. I don't have a job. What am I going to do?" I was rambling now and didn't make much sense.

Mother Green sat quietly for a minute, then finally said, "We think it would be best if you allowed some of our family to watch the children for a while. Maybe just the young ones. Harriet and Charles are in school, so they could stay with you, but the babies could stay with their aunts and uncles. Only until you get on your feet and figure out what you are going to do."

"What? Take my children away from me? They are all I have. How could you think such a thing? No – I'll not let that happen. I'll figure out something. No, No, No." I was getting frantic and Harry's parents could tell they weren't going to get anywhere with their idea.

Harry's father had been uncomfortable with the confrontation from the beginning. Finally, he spoke up. "Okay. Let's calm down and see what happens in the next couple days. But we are concerned about the welfare of the children."

I was shocked by what they were saying, but didn't have an answer. "Okay," I finally said. "Let's see what happens. No promises right now, but I'll think it over and have an answer soon."

Father had gone for a walk before the Greens came to visit. His timing was probably intentional since he returned soon after they left.

"Papa, can you believe it? The Greens want to take my children away from me."

He looked at me for a long time without saying anything, then sat next to me and gave a very serious look. "Mabel, dear, I've tried to stay out of the way and I know I haven't always been the best father for you, but I've been thinking about your situation. I think we need to talk."

"You've always been good to me Papa," I said. "I've always listened to you."

"What are you going to do?" he asked. "Do you have any idea what you are going to do without Harry?"

"No. Whenever I start thinking about living without Harry I start crying. I have five children including a five-month-old baby. I know I have to do something for them. But my mind is too confused right now. Part of me wants to go back to Montana, but it's not practical without Harry."

"And I can't help you there," Father said. "Besides, the bank may take the land pretty soon since we haven't paid anything on the loan."

"I don't want to stay here with the Greens. They're nice enough, but I don't want to be a burden on them. I don't want to be a burden on anyone. I want to live my own life, but I just can't figure things out."

"What do you think you could do?"

"Well, I could get a job in Jackson being a secretary or maybe a telephone operator, but I don't want to live in the city and I don't want to work for someone else. I need a job where I can be my own boss. I've had too much freedom over the years." My mind was spinning with options.

Papa was silent again. He had been thinking of something but wasn't sure if he should say it. "What about teaching?" he asked. "You taught the Sunday School in Cherry Ridge and you like children. You always talked about teaching in Montana."

"I'm not licensed or trained. Nobody will hire me around here."

"Where is the Richmond bravery? You sound scared. That's not the girl I raised." He was challenging my pride and it was working. "You've been to college – doesn't that count for something?"

"It was eighteen years ago. And I didn't graduate. I don't think that would be enough to get a teaching job. You're right, I do like teaching children, but I don't know if I can get a job."

"Why not give it a try? What would your mother say?"

"Mother would tell me to move on. 'Start another chapter' she would say. But I can't forget my past with Harry. He was so wonderful to me. But I've got to do something or I'll lose the children. I can't allow that to happen. I'm upset now, but I can't let anyone take my children away from me. They are all I have."

"Your mother and I didn't raise you to be a burden on society. We wanted you to be able to take care of yourself and your loved ones. You've done it in the past. You can do it in the future. Think of all the obstacles you overcame out on the prairie. The heat, the cold, the drought, the insects, the wildfires, the storms, the isolation – you battled all those things and more out there and overcame all of them. And you had love and friendship. You can do that again. You can overcome this obstacle and start over. You can do it."

My father had never talked to me that way. He had always been the domineering one. He had always been in charge, but here he was being a cheerleader and a supporter. He was pushing me to make up my own mind and do it my way. "Papa – you've never spoken like this before. Thank you. I needed to hear that. I will never forget Harry, but I must go on without him. He would want me to keep going. I can hear him telling me to get up and get busy. And Mama would be proud, too. I've got to do it. Thank you, Papa. I love you."

So it was decided. I would start looking for a job. Preferably a teaching job. I was convinced I could talk my way into a position in a small, rural area school. I reluctantly accepted the Greens' suggestion. I didn't like it, but could not think of another option. I needed time and I needed to know the children were okay. I used my insurance money to rent a small house in Union City and allowed the Greens to take the younger children until I could get my feet on the ground. Harriet and Charles stayed with neighbors in Union City and went to school so they wouldn't get behind. Rosemond went go to Detroit with Harry's sister, Rita, and her husband, Dutch. Bessabel – everyone was calling her Becky by now – stayed in Jackson with Hazel and her husband, while the baby, Bobby, was taken care of by brother-in-law Frank and his wife, Minnie, nearby in Parma. It was a terrible time. I missed my children and was determined to get a job quickly so I could get my family back together under one roof. The desire to reunite with my children drove me every day.

The Prairie Made Me: 1963

The rest of my story is pretty straightforward. I talked the superintendent of the Hanover Public Schools into giving me a teaching position on a trial basis. I told him my background and my current situation. When he hesitated I said, "If you don't hire me, I'll have to go on the public dole. I'm sure you don't want that." He laughed and seemed impressed by my audacity. When I promised to go back to college to get my teaching certification he gave me the job. I don't know if it was Richmond bravado, or my experience of listening to Harry talk his way into anything he wanted, but I put on quite a show for those folks in Hanover to convince them I could teach.

By September 1926, I had a teaching job and demanded my children back. It had been three months since my family was together and I wasn't going to let it go any longer. The Greens thought I was crazy. "No – You can't raise these five children by yourself. Who is going to watch them while you are teaching? Who is going to discipline them? You need some help."

"I will get by," was all I said. "I've done it before. I took care of the children on the prairie when Harry was gone. I've hunted for my food and grown crops to feed my family so I'm sure I can do it now. You aren't going to break up my family."

It probably created a divide with the Green family that never totally healed, but I was insistent and wasn't going to back down. I was going to get my family back together.

Father moved to the Masonic retirement home in Ypsilanti, Michigan. He was seventy-four and his health was failing. When he told me I said, "Papa, you can live with me. You can help me with the children."

"No," he said firmly. "I've lived with you off and on over the last twelve years. I'm old and tired and broke. Over the years I've made a lot of money but lost most of it speculating on land and gambling. I've loved every minute of the spending though," and made a little chuckle. "I can't keep up with your children any more, and I would just be another burden on you. I've been a Mason my entire life. I've paid for this retirement home in many ways. I'm going to take advantage of it."

"We will come visit. You can see your grandchildren whenever you want."

Papa stayed at the Masonic Home for almost three years, but when his health got worse and he could no longer pay anything to the Masons, we moved him to the Branch County Infirmary – better known as the "Poor Farm" – in Coldwater, Michigan, which was near my home in Litchfield. There, on February 27, 1931, Edmond C. Richmond died, not quite seventy-nine years old. Proud and stubborn to the end, he would never tell me he was hurting, but I could tell he was restless and in pain. He wanted to get out of the infirmary and go someplace. I'm sure he wanted to go back to the High Plains of Montana and look for a new fishing hole.

I went to college like I promised the Hanover superintendent. I attended Michigan Normal Teacher's College, now Eastern Michigan University. I was able to transfer some of my credits from the University of North Dakota and attended classes during the summers of 1927 and 1928. I graduated with an education degree and got my permanent Michigan Teacher's Certification on August 2, 1929. I was so proud to walk across the stage. Harriet and Charles were there to witness the ceremony. The rest of the children were at the Green farm.

The children and I moved to a small house in Hanover and I started a rather nomadic teaching career as I moved from one small rural school to another for the next thirty-two years. I taught in Hanover for two years, then moved to Litchfield, back to Hanover, then Montgomery, Camden, Reading, and finally Jonesville, Michigan. Every year I had to renew my contract and every year I looked for higher pay and better assignments. I taught all levels of elementary school, served as a student government adviser, and coached girls' basketball for over twenty years. My basketball teams at Litchfield, Montgomery, and Jonesville were very successful, winning district championships several times.

My "Chinook Coyotes" grew fast and were the light of my life. Each developed a distinctive personality and made contributions to our family. Family was always first – exactly as Harry would have wanted it. They were smart and did well in the Hanover schools. Harriet was a huge help, as she was not only big sister, but often my assistant with finances, shopping, cooking, and even discipline. Charles was my wild child. He was always running around town, would disappear in the woods for hours, loved to play sports, and had endless energy. He had Harry's red hair and I told everyone he was the spitting image of his father. He also had Harry's gift of gab and as he grew older could usually talk his way out of any problems he got into. Rosemond was an excellent student who skipped from second to fourth grade and graduated from high school when she was sixteen. Becky was smart and beautiful and by the time she was twelve had every boy in Hanover courting her. And Bobby, typical of the last child, wanted to do everything the other children did. He would follow Charles around town and tried to be included in every game he played, which of course infuriated Charles.

Living in a small town in Michigan during the Great Depression was eerily similar to living on the Great Plains in the 1920s. The entire community had to come together and help each other survive. No one was rich. We were all poor. The neighbors would share vegetables, fruits, eggs, and any other simple foodstuffs. My experiences on the homestead prepared me for whatever might happen during the Depression.

The children chipped in where they could. Harriet, Charles, and Rosemond all got jobs in town to help out. Harriet and Rosemond babysat and worked as telephone operators at night. Charles worked at the local gas station. Becky and Bobby were still too young, but they helped around the house when they could. The Depression brought us even closer together as a family. Like everyone else, we did not have much money. The school didn't even pay me with cash. I was paid in "chits" – pieces of paper I could use at the local stores for necessities.

Once one of the children was paid a nickel for a job. I let them decide how to spend it. They could buy five pieces of penny candy, or buy one egg. Of course, Bobby and Becky wanted the candy, but Harriet wanted to buy an egg. She realized we had the rest of the ingredients to make a cake, which would last much longer. We bought the egg.

Harriet married when she was sixteen. I think it was a way to get out of the house and cope with life on her own. She had always been my rock and I missed her help around the house. She had a son, then divorced her first husband. She remarried and had five more children while running a farm in southern Michigan.

Charles was one of the top athletes in town, playing football, basketball, and baseball. He was hell on wheels, and a rough and tumble sort of kid. He would boss his sisters and brothers around and play tricks on them. Then he would laugh and run away before they could retaliate. But he had a gentle heart and would do anything for anyone if they needed a favor. He bounced around to various jobs, then was called up with the first draft for World War II. He married before shipping overseas, served the entire war, was wounded twice, and recognized for bravery. After the war he became a successful realtor and raised two children.

All the children were good students, but Rosemond was tops in that category. She became the first of my children to go to college. After high school she received at Junior Dorcus Scholarship to attend Western Michigan Teacher's College – now Western Michigan University. She graduated in three years and received her diploma in 1939. She married in 1940, taught school for over thirty years and raised three boys.

Becky was the local beauty. She was eighteen when the war broke out and got a job as a secretary in Jackson. She shortly after the war ended she married a veteran who became a successful engineer. They raised two children.

Robert couldn't wait to be old enough to enlist and fight like his big brother. As soon as he turned seventeen he went down and signed up for the army. The war ended before he got to fight, much to my relief, but he was sent to Japan with the Occupation Forces and had quite a time over there. He came home older and wiser and finally ready to settle down. He married, had two sons, and started a successful business.

In 1963, at age seventy-three, I returned to Montana with Harriet to visit the homestead. I no longer had any claim to the land since the bank had foreclosed on Harry's loans in 1927. It had been owned by a number of people before Wes Baird, a local rancher, bought it up. Wes was an outgoing, helpful cowboy who was happy to entertain and take us to my homestead site. The Slonakers had moved to Havre but Bessie joined me for the trip.

It was wonderful to see Bessie and we immediately picked up conversation as if we were still neighbors. I choked back tears as we approached the homestead. The High Plains hadn't changed since the first time I saw them in 1910. The Bear Paw Mountains gave texture to the southern horizon and the ridgeline of Cherry Ridge became visible as we drove north. The dried creek beds reminded me of all the hard times we had getting water, and the vast fields of grain brought back memories of the hard, but rewarding work in the fields.

I recognized my place long before Wes said we were there. The house had been partially dismantled, with the western addition taken away and used for a granary on somebody's ranch. But the original structure was there, and the foundation Papa laid almost forty years earlier was clearly visible. I took one look around and started crying.

Wes, whom I had just met, asked if I was okay.

"Yes," I said with a smile, "I've never been happier. This is wonderful. Right now I am so full of wonderful memories I can't stop crying. This is the place that made me."

Bessie laughed. "We had some good times out here didn't we Mabel? Could anyone be closer than you and I were?

The work, the meals, the babies, the summers, and the winters? Through it all, I always knew you would be there for me."

"And you were always there for me," I said through more tears. "I think of the innocent, spoiled, little rich girl who arrived in Havre in 1910 and the changes I went through. I love this place. This land was supposed to be fun. It was supposed to make Father and me rich when we resold it. But that didn't happen. Instead, it made me tough and hard working. It taught me how to overcome impossible obstacles and appreciate how wonderful life really is.

"Think of it. When I first came here I didn't want for anything. Then Mama died and Father started wandering. I was on my own and had to make this place work. Then there was Leo, but I don't want to talk about him. I wouldn't have made it through all that without you Bessie."

"Ha, I didn't do that much," Bessie said. "You were tougher than you give yourself credit for. You were determined to make it. You wanted to show everyone you could when they said otherwise, and of course, you had Harry."

I laughed and gave her a hug. "Yes, Harry. He was loud, boisterous, mischievous, and sometimes annoying, but he was also spontaneous, exciting, honest, and so much fun. He would do anything for a friend. I loved that man. He was so good to me and so wonderful with the children. God, I miss him. You're right. I wouldn't have made it without Harry, but you were always there for me, my friend."

I went on, part reminiscing, part philosophizing. "Remember the great times we had? It's hard to describe to anyone who wasn't here. The beauty of this place is hypnotizing. I love Michigan, but nothing compares to the High Plains on a calm, cool, summer evening with the largest, bluest sky stretched out as you watch a brilliant sunset. Even when the weather was bad – a huge summer thunderstorm blowing across the never-ending prairie, or the winter blizzards blowing snow sideways, or the craziest, driest days – even then there was a certain beauty in the power of nature. It was like Mother Nature was testing you and trying to blow you off the prairie so she could have her virgin grasslands back. But that made me tougher and more determined to stay."

"And we did stay," said Bessie, "Longer than most. Longer than anyone thought we would. Now our children are grown and we both have a wonderful family of grandchildren. To think of that forty years ago would have made both of us laugh." And she laughed with the same contagious laugh she had when I first met her.

I was laughing too. "Oh, the things we've learned and seen since Harry and I left in 1925. We've all come a long way. We have been blessed, Bessie. Life had been good to us. I have always tried to live by my mother's advice to 'take every day as a challenge and face it with hope and acceptance of what it has to offer.' But it all comes back to this place. There is nothing that has been more important to me than this chunk of land. This place – the High Plains prairie land – made me and shaped me. I can never forget it and will never regret one minute of my time here."

Author's Notes

My grandmother, Mabel Richmond Green Lamb Holmes, died at the Spring Arbor, Michigan, Senior Citizens Center on March 8, 1979, having outlived Harry and two other husbands. When she died all five of her "Chinook Coyotes" were married, with fifteen grandchildren and twenty-three great-grandchildren.

Throughout our lives the family heard stories of the homestead, and since her death all of the children and many of the grandchildren and great-grandchildren have visited the homestead site. It has always been a place of reverence – with a bit of mystery – for the family.

This book began as an attempt to answer the family's age-old question – Why would a single, twenty-two-year-old, college educated woman who had previously lived a life of money and leisure, choose to homestead in the vast prairie of north central Montana by herself in 1913? It is a novelized reconstruction of her life using as much historical evidence, letters, and diary entries as possible. Most of the events actually happened, with only a few assumptions made based on situations presented, or avoided, in the evidence. My goal was to verify my grandmother's stories. For the most part those stories proved to be even better than she had told us over the years. As I read through her letters and researched the events of her life I realized how many obstacles she had overcome and how much she had struggled to raise her family. She never complained about any of it – she was upbeat and optimistic to the end. She continued to approach each day as her mother would have wanted her to – looking for opportunities and not looking back.

And she proved to be a very good writer in her own accord. In 1959, at age sixty-nine, she wrote an autobiographical magazine submission. Her words reflect her love of the High Plains.

In my memory I see vast fields of waving grass and grain, the prairies stretching for endless miles to the Little Rockies or four other ranges that formed my horizon, the royal purple mantle of acres of blossoming alfalfa or dazzling blue of flax.

Each of us has watched the terrifying glitter of an approaching cloud of grasshoppers on its way to destroy every green blade of grass or grain; battened our houses against a storm; groped our way through blinding blizzards by following a rope from house to barn; fought floods and prairie fires and endured the agony of waiting for a doctor. To balance these are the happy memories of loyal friendships, shared joys and blessed companionships. Every neighbor, even many miles away, was a friend and happiness and troubles were shared by all …

I would gladly welcome them all again to satisfy my enduring passion – homesteading. *

* Quoted from "The Enduring Passion" by Mabel R. Lamb, 1959

Source Notes

As much as possible I used historical sources for the stories and settings of this book. Most of the events have at least a small bit of evidence to support the story while some are speculation based on the timing and situation. For example, Mabel's presence at the suffragette speech and march in Havre cannot be verified, but Margaret Smith Hathaway did make a speech in Havre in October, 1914. It would be entirely possible, and within her character, for Mabel to attend her speech. A brief summary of the sources used are as follows:

Chapter 1: The Havre Land Office: 1913

1. Date based on copies of the final proof received from the U.S. National Archives and Records Administration and the Bureau of Land Management (BLM). The original claim was made March 13, 1913. Mabel claimed to have been in line for three days prior to the office opening.
2. Based on "An Enduring Passion" written by Mabel Richmond Green Lamb in 1959.

Chapter 2: E.C. Richmond

1. Reuben Richmond's movements are based on family genealogy research.

2. Founding of Richmond, MN from "An Enduring Passion" and "Richmond – A Brief History" in the August 2015 issue of *Crossings*, published by the Sterns History Museum.

3. The Dakota Wars of 1862 occurred throughout Minnesota. E. C. Richmond's adventures based on "An Enduring Passion".

4. Location of Richmond land and Lindbergh land based on early plot maps of Sterns County MN. Roger Paschke of the Melrose Historical Museum (MHS) was able to show me the land outside town.

5. Mary Isabel Richmond kept a scrapbook with hundreds of entries from the society pages of the local newspapers. Unfortunately, most of the clippings are small, four or five line entries, without much detail. Also, most of the clippings do not have a date or source to identify exactly where or when the information was written. Mabel retained this scrapbook after Belle Richmond's death. I have it at present. Most references to E. C.'s jobs and social life are based on entries in the scrapbook. This information will be referenced as the "Richmond Scrapbook".

6. Building Hotel Melrose: *Minneapolis Journal*, May 29, 1896 and *St. Paul News*, Oct. 27, 1896 and information obtained from Jeanne Wilber of the MHS.

7. Quotes from Richmond Scrapbook

8. Grand Master of Masons and election to president of city council from Richmond Scrapbook

9. Relationship to Ethan Allen based on genealogy research by Rick Green

10. Richmond Scrapbook contains many references to M. I. Richmond performing both musically and in plays.

11. Richmond Scrapbook has many references to her social calendar, church activities, and social functions.
12. Birth and death of Harriet Richmond based on Richmond Scrapbook, and cemetery information at Oak Hill Cemetery in Melrose, MN.
13. Birth Certificate verifies Mabel's birthday.
14. Baptism based on baptismal certificate given from Trinity Episcopal Church.

Chapter 3: Growing Up in Melrose: 1890-1906
1. Population from U. S. Census Records for 1900.
2. Descriptions of Melrose at turn of the century are based on articles in the *Melrose Beacon* and information from Jeanne Wilber of the MHS
3. Singing in church and dressing as Little Lord Fauntleroy based on the Richmond Scrapbook. Also a picture of Mabel as Little Lord Fauntleroy.
4. Bicycle award based on Richmond Scrapbook.
5. Toboggan making from MHS.
6. "Glass ball shooting" contest based on Richmond Scrapbook.
7. Quotes on train based on Mabel's description of her mother in letter to Rick Green.
8. M. I. Richmond's illness from Richmond Scrapbook
9. Background with Bohmer and Borgerding from Richmond Scrapbook and *Melrose Beacon* dated Oct. 3, 1902, Nov. 7, 1902, and Jan. 27, 1905.
10. Details for building of St. Boniface Church from Richmond Scrapbook, The MHS, and the book *Magnificent and Beautiful Structures*, by Jean Paschke detailing the history of St. Boniface/St. Michael's Church
11. Fire details from *St. Paul Times*, Oct. 29, 1898

12. Building of Church of St. Bridget in De Graff, MN from Richmond Scrapbook and National Historic Register
13. Building of Melrose School from *Melrose Beacon* and Richmond Scrapbook

Chapter 4: Havre Land Office

1. Story of being first in line from "An Enduring Passion"

Chapter 5: Leaving Melrose

1. Grand Forks tornado from *New York Times* 6/18/1887 and GenDisasters.com
2. Building in Osnabrock and Sarles, ND from Richmond Scrapbook, and *Melrose Beacon* Oct. 3, 1902, and Nov. 7, 1902,
3. E. C. Richmond's presence in ND by 1904 obtained from Richmond Scrapbook
4. Purchase of 480 acre farm in ND from *Melrose Beacon*, Oct. 30, 1908
5. Trips to Sarles Hotel from Richmond Scrapbook
6. 1905 trip to Grand Forks from Richmond Scrapbook
7. Construction of banks from *Grand Forks Evening Times* Sept.17, 1906, Nov. 6, 1906, and Dec. 6, 1906.
8. Reference to Mabel's sixteenth birthday party in Richmond Scrapbook

Chapter 6: Grand Forks: 1906-1910

1. Address of 212 Chestnut St. from *1910 Polk City Directory* for Grand Forks, ND, and *Grand Forks Evening Times* Apr. 20, 1910.
2. Mabel on GF High girls' basketball team from team photo.

3. Getting the contract for St. Michael's from Richmond Scrapbook and Melrose Beacon Apr. 3, 1908, *The Pioneer Times*, June 19, 1908.
4. Summer in Melrose from Richmond Scrapbook
5. Construction of St. Michael's from the *Grand Forks Evening Times*, Oct. 9, 1908, Nov.23, 1908, and Oct. 16, 1909.
6. High School graduation from *Grand Forks Daily Herald*, June 4, 1908 and *Melrose Beacon*, June 5, 1908.
7. Story of returning of wallet from *Bismarck Daily Tribune*, July 17, 1908.
8. Description and consecration ceremony of St. Michael's from the *Grand Forks Evening Times* Oct. 16, 1909.
9. Building roundhouse from the *Grand Forks Evening Times,*
10. Attendance at University of North Dakota from UND records and Mabel's report card
11. 1904 fire in Havre and growth of Great Northern from Havre town history

Chapter 7: Havre: 1910-1913

1. Frank Buttery and construction of Buttery Dept. Store from *Harlem Enterprise*, Sept.22, 1910, and Nov. 10, 1910,
2. Leo's high school career from *Havre Enterprise* June 6, 1917.
3. History and physical description of Havre from Havre history and Havre City Library
4. M. I. Richmond's trip to Rochester, MN and Mayo Clinic for a "personal operation" from Richmond Scrapbook and *Grand Forks Evening Times*, July 3, 1909.

5. M. I. Richmond's 1910 trip to Seattle from Richmond Scrapbook and *Grand Forks Evening Times*, October 5, 1910

6. Death and funeral of Cynthia Richmond from Richmond Scrapbook

7. Trip to Glacier National Park from *Grand Forks Evening Times*, Sept. 11, 1911.

Chapter 8: Land!

1. Three claims filed under the Desert Land Act based on Record of Patients.

2. Lloyd and Bruce Smith named on patients as "assignee". Apparently, assignees would take out the original claim, then sign it over to the settler for a minimal fee. In this case they were the assignees for Mary Isabelle's and Mabel's claims under the Desert Land Act. Advertisements in the *Havre Enterprise* and *Fort Benton River Press* list them as surveyors.

3. E.C.'s claim for homestead based on Record of Patients.

Chapter 9: Homesteading

1. March 12, 1913 based on National Archives paperwork and application for proof.

2. Description of land based on Record of Patients and National Archives paperwork

3. Quotes about riches of Montana from histories of Montana and homesteading.

4. Leo's claim to 160 acres based on maps at Blaine County Museum.

Chapter 10: Death of My Soul

1. M. I. Richmond's death from *Grand Forks Evening Times*, June 2, 1913, *Melrose Beacon*, June 6, 1913, and death certificate.

2. Obituary in *Melrose Beacon*, June 6, 1913 description of funeral.

Chapter 11: The High Plains

1 Size of homestead house and barn based on National Archives paperwork and "An Enduring Passion"

2 Ten acres plowed based on National Archives paperwork

3 First night in house from National Archives paperwork

4 November move to Havre based on National Archives paperwork

Chapter 12: Leo and Me

Mabel kept a diary for much of her early years in Montana, however, her 1914 Diary is the only one still intact. That is in my possession and was the source for many of the events and quotes in the early years of homesteading. Some dates and situations were moved around a little to keep the story moving, however, they are all mentioned at one time or another during 1914. I will just reference the 1914 Diary.

1. Lifestyle in Havre from 1914 Diary

2. Religious conflict from 1914 Diary

3. Winter weather including temp of -30 from 1914 Diary

4. Leo's trip to homestead in winter from 1914 Diary

5. Seeing Leo on sidewalk, argument, and make-up from 1914 Diary

6. E. C.'s birthday, filing first year paperwork, from 1914 Diary

7. Quote "What a wonderful day..." from 1914 Diary

Chapter 13: The Prairie Made Me

1. E. C.'s office on 4th St. based on Havre city directory for 1913-1914.

2. Mabel's purchase of house on 5th Ave. and 7th St. based on paperwork at Hill County Clerk's office.

3. Names and location of neighbors based on homestead maps at Blaine County Museum.

4. Leo's present of Buck and improvements to house based on 1914 Diary

5. Planting 10 acres of flax and plowing 30 from National Archives paperwork

6. Improvements to farm from National Archives paperwork.

7. Having piano at the farm from 1914 Diary

8. Community meals, dances, problems with car based on 1914 Diary

9. First mention of Harry Green in April 1914 Diary entry

10. Walking from Leo's house to Mabel's house in the dark from 1914 Dairy

11. Trip to Havre for Easter, baptism, and return to the homestead from 1914 Diary

12. First year of Mother's death and quote from 1914 Diary

Chapter 14: A Loss and A Change: 1914

1. This chapter is a very speculative chapter. There is no mention of Mabel's pregnancy or miscarriage in any of the sources, however, her 1914 diary has six weeks of pages deliberately cut out from early June to mid July

1914. I assumed it must have been a major event for it to be destroyed. Shortly after the cut out section a diary entry says, "We've had much happiness and one great sorrow to bind us inseparably." The thought of "one great sorrow" and a bit of "author's license" led me to make up the story of the pregnancy and miscarriage. I hope family members looking for accuracy will forgive me for a bit of fiction and imagination.

Chapter 15: Ranching and Politics of the High Plains
1. Temperature in June from 1914 Diary
2. Brushfire from 1914 Diary
3. Four day rain and aftermath from 1914 Diary
4. Harry Green and chickens from 1914 Diary
5. Discomfort of staying alone and quotes from 1914 Diary
6. Fourth anniversary quote from 1914 Diary

Chapter 16: Complications: 1915
1. Moving back in November from National Archives paperwork
2. Social life in Havre, desire to return to ranch and return trip all based on 1914 Diary
3. Quotes about friends and neighbors from 1914 Diary
4. Harbolt diverting water from 1914 Diary
5. Planting 40 acres and plowing 20 from on National Archives paperwork
6. Harvest of 240 bushels of flax from National Archives paperwork
7. Leo's temper about falling into cactus and bad haircut from 1914 Diary
8. Quote "Love is bigger than pride..." from 1914 Diary

Chapter 17: Moving On

1. Background of Harry Green from family genealogy and census records
2. Reason for adding "E" to end of name based on letter to Hazel in 1919. No date.

Chapter 18: A Prairie Child

1. Harry Green patent approval from Record of Patients
2. Application for Z/T brand from branding records
3. Letter to Hazel, May 1916
4. Birth of Harriet based on birth certificate and family genealogy
5. Marriage on August 29th based on Blaine County Marriage license from Blaine County Clerk and family history

Chapter 19: Looking Back/Looking Ahead

1. Backdating of marriage from certificate issued by St. Mark's Episcopal Church listing wedding as Dec. 7, 1915
2. Letter to Hazel dated Sept. 10, 1916
3. Yield of 1916 harvest from letters and National Archives paperwork
4. Purchase of tractor from letter to Hazel dated Nov. 10, 1916
5. Thanksgiving dinner based on letters to MI dated late 1916 (No specific date)

Chapter 20: Proving Up: 1917

1. Weather in Jan./Feb. 1917 based on undated letter to Hazel.

2. Quotes about baby Harriet based on letters to Hazel dated Nov. 10, 1916
3. Renting school section based on letters to Hazel dated Nov. 10, 1916
4. Quote of "if there is trouble..." based on letters summer of 1919.
5. Harry's draft status based on Draft Registration Card
6. 71 Blaine County boys going to war based on undated letter to Hazel.
7. Frank and WWI service based on family genealogy
8. Details of proving Mabel's claim from BLM Application for Land Patent and National Archives paperwork.
9. Weather in July 1917 based on letters to Hazel dated July 25, 1917
10. Harry selling land based on letter to Hazel undated but from winter 1917.
11. Rode sleigh into Havre based on undated letter to Hazel.

Chapter 21: Family and Farming

1. Charles Green's birth verified by birth certificate
2. Trip to Michigan and return through Chicago and Melrose based on letter dated March 30, 1919
3. Drive from Chinook to range with neighbors based on letter dated March 30, 1919.
4. Price of seed wheat in Canada based on undated letter of spring 1919.
5. Charles being sick and quotes based on letter of summer 1919.
6. Start of school and Sunday school based on letter of summer 1919

7. Playing cards in winter based on letter dated Jan 24, 1920.

Chapter 22: A Dangerous Prank

1. Going to dances at Cherry Ridge Grange Hall based on letter dated Oct. 13, 1916
2. E. C. Working as timber consultant from the Olympia, WA newspaper *Washington Standard*, July 21, 1921.
3. Harry's arrest from *Great Falls Tribune*, Great Falls, MT. Feb. 12, 1921
4. Harry jailing and bail based on Blaine County Records and transcript of the Eighteenth Judicial District of Montana, Blaine Country Clerk's Office, dated Feb. 28, 1921.
5. Harry throwing hide out of car window is from a local legend
6. Rosemond's birth certified by birth certificate
7. Results of Harry's trial based on Blaine County Circuit Court Records dated June 14, 1921.

Chapter 23: Bessabel

1. Harry's bought with typhoid based on "Robie's Recollections"
2. Origin of name of Bessabel based on "Robie's Recollections"

Chapter 24: Drought and Hard Times

1. Based on letters to sister Hazel in 1919 and 1920.

Chapter 25: To Michigan: 1925
1. Gathering with Slonakers and other families based on pictures and family legend.
2. Robert Green birth verified by birth certificate.
3. Uncle Hal's background based on family genealogy
4. Tootsie shying from trees in Michigan based on "Robie's Recollections"

Chapter 26: My World Turned Upside Down
1. Events of July 7, 1926 based on "Robie's Recollections"
2. Harry's death based on Cook County IL Death Certificate and Jackson *Citizen Patriot* obituary.
3. Funeral events and saving lock of hair based on "Robie's Recollections"
4. Children being separated and staying with family based on "Robie's Recollections"

Chapter 27: The Prairie Made Me: 1963
1. Mabel talking her way into a teaching job in Hanover based on "Robie's Recollections"
2. E. C. Richmond's death based on death certificate
3. Mabel's graduation from EMU based on transcript from Michigan State Normal College, Ypsilanti, MI. Aug. 2, 1929.
4. Mabel's teaching and coaching career based on Michigan Public School Employees Retirement Fund dated June 26, 1959.
5. Children working during the Depression and being paid in chits based on "Robie's Recollections"
6. Deciding what to do with a nickel based on "Robie's Recollections"

7. Mabel's trip to Montana in 1963 based on photographs and family knowledge.

Author's Notes:

1. Mabel's death verified by death certificate and obituary

About the Author

Tom Laughlin is a retired history teacher and coach living in Grand Haven, Michigan. He taught American and European History and coached varsity cross country and eighth grade basketball for over thirty years. He is also a retired Lieutenant Colonel after twenty-three years of active and reserve duty in the army. His first book, *Summer of '71,* was a memoir of hitchhiking across the United States in 1971. *Portrait of a Prairie Woman* is based on the life and adventures of his maternal grandmother living on a homestead in Montana. He and his wife Jackie have two sons who are married, with two beautiful grandchildren each. Jackie and Tom still enjoy traveling through life together.